3 STEPS TO INCREDIBLE HEALTH!

VOLUME 2

JOEL FUHRMAN, M.D.

PUBLISHED BY

ᑲᑭ

Gift of Health Press

OTHER BOOKS BY JOEL FUHRMAN, M.D.

Eat To Live

Eat For Health

Disease-Proof Your Child

Cholesterol Protection For Life

Fasting and Eating For Health

Published by Gift of Health Press, Flemington, New Jersey.

Contact:
Joel Fuhrman, M.D.
4 Walter Foran Boulevard, Suite 409
Flemington, NJ 08822

Publisher's Note:
Keep in mind that results vary from person to person. Some people have a medical history and/or condition that may warrant individual recommendations and in some cases drugs and even surgery. Do not start, stop, or change medication without professional medical advice, and do not change your diet if you are ill or on medication except under the supervision of a competent physician. Neither this, nor any other book, is intended to take the place of personalized medical care or treatment.

Printed in the United States of America

Design: Robyn Rolfes, Creative Syndicate, Inc.
Cover Design: Savita Naidu
Cover Photograph: Sandra Nissen

Library of Congress Control Number: 2011904330

ISBN: 978-0-9799667-8-1

First Edition

DEDICATION

This book is dedicated to every American who is suffering with chronic disease, especially those who have been told that their problems are genetic and that drugs or invasive interventions are the only answers.

Even though the powerful therapeutic benefits of superior nutrition have been well documented in the scientific literature, this information has not been made available to the general public. Depriving people of the right to know that recoveries are possible through superior nutrition leads to needless suffering and—all too often—premature death.

People have a right to know that they have a choice. They have a right to know that they do not have to suffer and die prematurely from medical conditions that are easily prevented and reversed. If you think you deserve better health, if you want to reduce medical expenditures and avoid surgeries and medications, or if you just want to live longer—with good health and mental facilities intact, this book is dedicated to you with the hope that the menus, recipes, and other information presented will be of help to you as you transform your life.

Contents

PREFACE

I wrote this book to fill the desperate need for healthful high-nutrient menus and recipes. Most recipe books focus on gustatory pleasure, but there is an ever growing number that purport to focus on healthful foods and meals. Sadly, even the so-called health cookbooks fall far short when it comes to actually helping people build, recover, and maintain health. The recommendations are too timid; they either don't address the most important changes needed, or they don't go far enough to make any measurable difference. In other words, they don't work.

The recipes and menus in this book do work. That's because they are based on an approach to eating that has been scientifically shown to dramatically help people both prevent and recover from most of the chronic illnesses that Americans develop. What's more, it has been shown to consistently promote healthy and *permanent* weight loss. For more detail about the research and experience behind the design of my high-nutrient diet program, please refer to *3 Steps to Incredible Health, Volume 1.*

You probably know as well as everyone else that obesity and other dietary factors are major contributors to America's growing epidemic of heart disease, diabetes, osteoarthritis, lupus and other autoimmune diseases, dementia, and even cancer. But identifying the problem is not the same as solving it. To solve this problem, we need to do the work of making substantial changes. This book gives you the dietary tools— menus, recipes, and strategies—you need to build a new, healthier life for yourself.

In addition to all the research data, more than twenty years of experience working with patients has taught me that unless a person adopts a healthful, long-term approach to diet and the lifestyle factors that accompany eating, there is little hope of their preventing or recovering from chronic disease. By age fifty, most Americans are being treated with medication for one or more diseases, almost all of which could have been prevented. As any doctor can tell you, drugs cannot grant you excellent health and protection from disease and suffering. Thirty-eight percent of Americans die of heart attacks and strokes.

The most effective health care is proper self-care.

In 2003, my bestselling book *Eat To Live* (revised in 2011) presented the high-nutrient approach to eating for the first time. Since then, I have received countless letters and e-mails of gratitude from people whose lives have changed dramatically. It feels good to know that my recommendations are helping people, but the success stories continually remind me of a very important fact: Even people who enthusiastically embrace dietary change face significant hurdles that need to be overcome.

In my medical practice, I have noticed that the people who achieve the greatest success are those who initially make substantial changes, followed by continual, step-by-step improvements to their diets over time. If possible, throw away all the unhealthful foods from your kitchen, and start your new dietary life immediately. Most people do better with decisive change, followed by steady, determined, step-by-step improvements. Don't worry about being "perfect" immediately. This book will give you the information and encouragement you need for your ultimate success.

It is my desire to help as many people as possible change their dependence—even addiction—to the standard American diet (SAD) so that they can enjoy vibrant health throughout a long, healthy, and enjoyable life. The menus, recipes, and eating strategies in this book are designed to give you the guidance and the helping hand necessary for you to transform yourself and to begin living a healthier life than you ever thought possible.

Acknowledgements

I had assistance from many people in developing this book. My wife, Lisa, reads everything I write and helps me immensely. My editors, Jim Lennon and Susan Taylor Lennon, have done another fantastic job. Robyn Rolfes designed the book, and Savita Naidu designed the diagrams and cover. Deana Ferrari, Ph.D., assisted with research, and Linda Popescu, R.D., worked with me on *Dr. Fuhrman's Nutrient Density Scores,* menus, and recipes. Some of the recipes were contributed by members at DrFuhrman.com, and I appreciate their generosity and desire to help others. The contributions of my executive team, Janice McDonnell-Marra and Dominic Ambrosio, were invaluable. Finally, I want to thank my children—Talia, Jenna, Cara, and Sean— who serve as loyal taste-testers for my *unique* recipe ideas and who support me in so many ways.

The single most important aspect of the menus and recipes in this book is that they are extremely high in micronutrients. That is why I call it the *high-nutrient diet*. My program is designed to optimize micronutrient density, micronutrient diversity, and micronutrient completeness. In addition to the typical vitamins and minerals that everybody talks about, these recipes provide thousands of other phytonutrients that are important for maximizing immune function, preventing cancer and other diseases, and increasing healthy longevity.

Lots of diet plans call for counting calories, eliminating some foods and adding others, but none, except this one, asks you to strive for more micronutrients in your diet. In fact, eating foods that have a high nutrient-to-calorie ratio will be central to your success. This goal is so important that I have created *Dr. Fuhrman's Nutrient Density Scores*, a listing of foods ranked according to their micronutrient-per-calorie ratios. Eat enough of the higher ranking foods, and you will start to optimize your health potential. You also will lose weight.

Even though you won't be counting calories, and you'll be eating a lot of food, my high-nutrient diet will let you lose all the weight you want. A recent medical study confirmed that the nutritional program presented in this book is the most effective weight-loss plan ever documented in medical literature, especially if you have a lot of weight to lose.[1] After two years, participants lost more weight than the subjects of any other study in medical history, and they kept it off. Their success is due in part to the fact that as people increase the micronutrient quality of their diet, their hunger lessens and their desire to overeat is curtailed.[2]

While you almost surely will lose your excess weight, this book is not a weight-loss book. It provides you with 151 delicious and healthful recipes and instruction on high-nutrient eating that you will use for the rest of your life. The goal is for you to become incredibly healthy; losing weight is a pleasant side effect.

High-nutrient recipes

In my companion book, *3 Steps to Incredible Health, Volume 1,* I explain why the low-nutrient diet that most people consume leads initially to food cravings and overeating, and ultimately to diseases such as allergies, asthma, acne, headaches, high blood pressure, diabetes, reflux esophagitis, lupus, kidney insufficiency, angina, cardiomyopathy, and multiple sclerosis. The recipe for good health and a long, disease-free life is to plan your eating around foods that have a high nutrient-to-calorie ratio—foods that are high in micronutrients and low in calories. Naturally, the recipes in this book all feature high-nutrient foods and food tips to help you choose foods and design meals that have the highest nutrient density.

Getting started

To make it as easy as possible for you to start eating better right away, I've devised menu plans that offer three levels of superior nutrition. They start with Level 1 and move up progressively to Level 3, the most effective level for reversing disease and maximizing health and longevity. Of course, I hope you move quickly to the highest level, but all levels are excellent, especially when compared to the low-nutrient standard American diet (SAD). Pick a level and stay with it, or gradually work your way up. It's your choice. The menu plans allow you the option of moving back and forth between levels, while making small but significant additions or subtractions to your diet.

One of the ways in which this step-by-step approach is helpful is that as you experiment with high-nutrient eating, your taste buds have a chance to gradually adapt to the new flavors and textures. Your body also needs to adjust to the fact that you will be eating a lot of food; the program for all levels is high-nutrient, but low-calorie, so you don't have to worry about how much food you eat.

As you already know—you are what you eat. To be your best, you must eat the best. This book offers you examples of the very best meals you can eat and teaches you the nutritional principles you need to know to eat healthfully and enjoy the benefits for the rest of your life.

A word of caution

The dietary approach I recommend is so effective at lowering weight, blood pressure, and blood sugar that you may need to have your medication adjusted so that you are not overmedicated. If your blood sugar or blood pressure improves dramatically and medications are not reduced or eliminated, it could be harmful to your health. Please consult with your physician.

1. Fuhrman J, Sarter B, Campbell TC. "Effect of a high-nutrient diet on long-term weight loss: a retrospective chart review." *Altern Ther Health Med* 2008;14(3): publication pending.

2. Fuhrman J, Sarter B, Glaser D, Accocella S. "Changing perceptions of hunger on a high nutrient density diet." *Nutrition Journal* 2010;9:51.

SECTION 1

THE FOUNDATIONS OF
HEALTH EXCELLENCE

THE HIGH-NUTRIENT DIET

The most important building block of health is nutrition. Without superior nutrition, your ability to live life to the fullest is impossible. Before we get to the menus and recipes, I want to describe the foundation upon which they have been designed. While other dietary programs focus on various combinations of *macro*nutrients—proteins, carbohydrates, and fats, my high-nutrient diet focuses on getting large amounts of *micro*nutrients—vitamins, minerals, and especially phytochemicals—into your diet. For ideal health, you need to get both kinds of nutrients, but the standard American diet (SAD) contains too many macronutrients and not enough micronutrients.

A micronutrient-rich diet supplies 14 different vitamins, 25 different minerals, and more than 1,000 phytochemicals, plant-based chemicals that have profound effects on human cell function and the immune system. It turns out that foods that are naturally rich in these nutrients are also rich in fiber and water and are naturally low in calories. These high-nutrient, low-calorie foods provide what your body needs to maximize its self-healing and self-repairing mechanisms.

The need to dramatically increase the micronutrients in your diet is so important that I've created an equation that makes it crystal clear. I call it my Health Equation.

Dr Fuhrman's Health Equation: H = N/C

Your future Health (H) will increase as your Nutrient (N)* to Calorie (C) ratio increases.

* Nutrient (N) refers to *micro*nutrients.

Your health is dependent on the nutrient-per-calorie density of your diet (micronutrients consumed divided by calories consumed). This straightforward mathematical formula is the basis of nutritional science and nutritional healing.

To make it easy for you to see which foods have the highest nutrient-per-calorie density, I have ranked the nutrient levels of many common foods using my *Dr. Fuhrman's Nutrient Density Scores*. The highest ranking a food can get is 100. The scores provide a simple way to help you identify and eat larger amounts of high-nutrient foods. The higher the number and the greater percentage of those foods in your diet, the better your health will be. Take a look at the scores. How do the foods in your current diet rate?

DR. FUHRMAN'S NUTRIENT DENSITY SCORES

Mustard greens	100	Mushrooms	35
Watercress	100	Tomato	33
Kale	100	Pomegranate	30
Turnip greens	100	Carrots	30
Collard greens	100	Blueberries	27
Brussels sprouts	90	Orange	27
Bok choy	85	Grapes	24
Spinach	82	Edamame	21
Arugula	77	Cherries	21
Cabbage	59	Tofu	20
Flaxseed	55	Sesame seeds	19
Broccoli	52	Sunflower seeds	16
Cauliflower	51	Artichoke	16
Romaine	45	Lentils	14
Green bell pepper	41	Cantaloupe	12
Onions	37	Peaches	11
Asparagus	36	Kidney beans	11
Strawberries	35	Walnuts	10

Iceberg lettuce 10
Pistachio nuts 9
Cucumber 9
Sweet potato 9
Green peas 7
Almonds 7
Pineapple 7
Avocado 6
Cashews 6
Apple 5
Mango 5
Peanut butter 5
Corn 4
Bananas 3
Brown rice 3
Oatmeal 3
White potato 2
Salmon 2

Skim milk 2
Low-fat plain yogurt 2
Whole wheat bread 2
Olive oil 2
Apple juice 1
White bread 1
Chicken breast 1
Eggs 1
White pasta 1
Shrimp 1
Ground beef, 85% lean .... -4
Feta cheese .... -5
Low-fat cheddar cheese .... -6
Potato chips .... -9
French fries .... -9
Vanilla ice cream .... -9
Cola .... -10

::············· **DR. FUHRMAN'S NUTRIENT DENSITY SCORES** ·············::

To determine the scores, an equal-calorie serving of each food was evaluated. The following nutrients were included in the evaluation: calcium, carotenoids (beta carotene, alpha carotene, lutein, zeaxanthin, and lycopene), fiber, folate, glucosinolates, magnesium, selenium, vitamin C, vitamin E, zinc, phytosterols, resistant starch, flavonoids, plus ORAC score. ORAC (Oxygen Radical Absorbance Capacity) is a measure of the antioxidant or radical-scavenging capacity of a food. For consistency, nutrient quantities were converted from their typical measurement conventions (mg, mcg, IU) to a percentage of their Reference Daily Intake (RDI). For nutrients that have no RDI, goals were established based on available research and current understanding of the benefits of these factors. Points were added if the food item was anti-angiogenic or contained organosulfides, aromatase inhibitors, or resveratrol. Points were subtracted if the food item contained trans fat, an excessive amount of saturated fat, cholesterol, or sodium, or was a refined or processed food with harmful additives. To make it easier to compare foods, the raw point totals were converted (multiplied by the same number) so that the highest ranking food (mustard greens) received a score of 100, and the other foods received lower scores accordingly.

Green vegetables have the highest scores, so it is no wonder that they have the best association with lower rates of cancer and heart disease. The foods that Americans eat most often are the ones with the lower scores. As you move your diet toward the foods with the higher scores, you will begin to dramatically enhance your health. The recipes and menus in this book will help you achieve this goal.

In addition to the Levels 1, 2, and 3 menu choices available, there are some foods that you can eat in relatively unlimited quantities. If you can learn to make your meals mostly from the foods in the higher categories, you will be giving your health a terrific jump start.

Here are some high-nutrient foods that can be eaten in nearly unlimited quantities (without overeating, of course):

Leafy green vegetables
romaine lettuce, leaf lettuces, kale, collards, Swiss chard, cabbage, spinach, bok choy, parsley

Solid green vegetables
artichokes, asparagus, broccoli, brussels sprouts, cabbage, celery, cucumber, kohlrabi, okra, peas, green peppers, snow peas, string beans, zucchini

Non-green, high-nutrient vegetables
beets, eggplant, mushrooms, onions, tomatoes, peppers, bamboo shoots, water chestnuts, cauliflower, squash, carrots

Beans and legumes
red kidney beans, adzuki beans, chickpeas, pinto beans, cowpeas, navy beans, cannellini beans, soybeans, lentils, white beans, lima beans, pigeon peas, black-eyed peas, black beans, split peas

Fresh fruits
apples, apricots, blackberries, blueberries, grapes, kiwis, mangoes, nectarines, all melons, oranges, peaches, pears, persimmons, pineapples, plums, raspberries, strawberries, tangerines

In addition to eating more micronutrient-rich foods, you need to eat fewer macronutrients. Every nutritional scientist in the world agrees that moderate caloric restriction slows the aging process, prevents the development of chronic diseases, and extends life span. This has been tested in every species of animal, including primates. There is no controversy; Americans are eating themselves to death with too many calories. To change this, we must do three things:

Eat less fat.

Eat less protein.

Eat less carbohydrate.

As you embark on your new dietary journey, keep in mind that there are three vital components to high-level health. Each of the three components—nutritional, physical, and social—must be considered.

- Nutritional component—Make every calorie count as you strive for maximum nutrition. This book and *3 Steps to Incredible Health, Volume 1* provide all of the information you need.

- Physical component—Make physical exercise a part of your normal routine. Joining a gym is a great bonus, but learn to take advantage of all of your opportunities to exercise—such as taking the stairs instead of the elevator and, when possible, walking instead of riding. You may find that exercise is easier and more pleasurable as your health improves and you start losing weight.

- Social component—Develop the confidence and self-esteem necessary to deal with unhealthful influences. A healthy mindset is a prerequisite for a healthy lifestyle, and the best way to develop it is to surround yourself with people who engage in and support your health.

Overcoming bad habits

Let's face it: Bad habits and addictions can make dietary changes diffi-
cult. Fortunately, it only takes a few seconds of determination to say
an emphatic "no" to the addiction and "yes" to your new healthful lifestyle. I have observed thousands of patients suffer through temporary
discomforts while their bodies were eliminating the toxic aftermath of
unhealthful diets. This is normal, and it is a small price to pay for the
improved health and enhanced joy for life that will soon follow.

Let's talk briefly about food addictions and how to get beyond
them. Modern foods are designed to seduce your taste buds. The artifi-
cially concentrated flavors of processed foods and added salt stimulate
the pleasure centers in the brain and lead your taste buds astray. It
doesn't take long before you lose your taste for whole natural foods.
Fortunately, sticking to the recipes in this book (and even simpler
meals you can make yourself) helps your taste buds bounce back. It
may take time to reset your taste receptors to appreciate the more
subtle flavors of whole natural foods, but your taste and flavor sensitiv-
ity will improve tremendously over time.

Some of the recipes in this book will taste great to you right away.
For example, my healthful sorbets and "ice creams" are the perfect
substitute for your craving of cold sweets. When you find yourself
missing something from the past, treat yourself to something good
from the present. The main thing is not to give up. The only failure is
to stop trying.

The ability to eat right consistently requires some planning. Set
aside time to buy and/or prepare good-tasting, healthful foods so that
you will have them around you at all times. This minimizes temptation. Unfortunately, extremely few restaurants make eating this way
convenient, so it might make sense to put off eating out until you feel
confident making healthful meals for yourself at home. As you gain
proficiency at improvising meals in your own kitchen, you'll be better
prepared to ask a restaurant to improvise a meal for you.

Eliminate temptation

In a perfect world, you would get rid of all the unhealthful food in
your kitchen. If it's not in the house, you won't have to fight unneces-

sary temptation. But if your family is continuing to eat the old diet, create a separate area in the pantry and refrigerator for your foods. It certainly isn't easy to eat well while still having to make unhealthful foods for your family, but don't despair. By making yourself look and feel healthier, you are setting a tremendously good example. Stock up on nutrient-rich foods so that you always have them available. Having good foods within easy reach is one of the most powerful strategies for achieving success.

Three meals per day

For maximum success, it is best to stick to a three-meal-per-day format, without snacking. Lots of people thrive on two meals per day, too. Unless you are an athlete or a physical laborer, you probably don't burn enough calories to justify snacking. If you eat enough at your regular meals, there should be no need for snacking.

Here are some helpful hints to combat snacking:

- Eat a salad or raw vegetables with a dip to start both lunch and dinner.

- Keep lots of frozen fruits and vegetables and pre-washed fresh foods in your home.

- Have cooked greens or soups with greens at every lunch and dinner.

- Don't eat after 8:00 p.m.

- Have a fruit sorbet or fruit dessert after dinner, and then clean the kitchen, clean your teeth, and end eating for the day.

Reading labels

Shopping for your new way of eating may require some new skills. It's easy to shop for the highest-nutrient foods; they are mostly in the produce aisle and frozen food section. But it's important to read the labels on other foods. You can use all spices and herbs except for salt. When using condiments, mustard is okay if unsalted mustard is available, but pickled foods typically contain too much salt and should be avoided. If you love ketchup or tomato sauce, you may find a lower calorie, low-salt ketchup and tomato sauce at the health food store.

The most important part of the label is the ingredient list. Avoid foods that list white flour (often called wheat flour) and any type of sweetener, such as corn syrup, among the first few ingredients. Ingredients are listed on the label according to quantity, in descending order based on weight (from most to least). As a general rule of thumb, don't buy foods that have long lists of ingredients that you cannot pronounce. Be sure to read the ingredients even when purchasing foods from a health food store. And don't be fooled by nice sounding but misleading phrases like "natural fruit flavors," "with real fruit juice," "all natural ingredients," "no artificial preservatives," or "no artificial ingredients." These are advertising words, not scientific ones. *3 Steps to Incredible Health, Volume 1* goes into a lot of detail about how to pick the best foods, but, for now, all you need to do is use the recipes in this book.

When looking at labels, you need to pay special attention to sodium levels. A lot of sodium is "hidden" in processed foods. When you see the word "salt" on a food label, you know that salt is in the product. But baking soda and monosodium glutamate (MSG) contain sodium, too. Try to avoid products with brine, disodium phosphate, garlic salt, onion salt, sodium alginate, sodium benzoate, sodium caseinate, sodium citrate, sodium hydroxide, sodium nitrate, sodium pectinate, sodium proprionate, and sodium sulfite. Also avoid anything using the words "pickled," "cured," "broth," and "soy sauce." They all indicate high sodium. If you are eating processed foods, they should have less than 1 mg of sodium per calorie. If a serving of food provides 100 calories and it contains 400 mg of sodium, it is a high-sodium food, and you should avoid it. If a serving of the food has 100 calories and has less than 100 mg of sodium, it is a much better choice.

DR. FUHRMAN'S COOKING SCHOOL

Now that you understand the basic principles of high-nutrient eating, here are some essential cooking tips and tools for preparing the meals and recipes in this book.

Helpful tools

Your journey to excellent health will be made much easier if you have all of the tools you need in your kitchen. You may already have everything you need to start cooking, but take a few minutes to make sure you are supplied with these important basics:

- Food chopper or a good knife set

- Vegetable juicer

- High-powered blender

- Pressure cooker

- Wok with cover or large pan with cover

A powerful blender such as the Vita-Mix is very helpful. Only the more expensive, high-powered blenders will be able to make fruit sorbets from frozen fruits and creamy dressings and dips from nuts and seeds. They also can blend vegetables effortlessly for your fruit or green smoothies. It is a good investment that will last a lifetime. Cooking soups and stews with a pressure cooker produces healthful and tasty food fast. You can prepare a soup or bean dish in less than half the time. A vegetable juicer is great for preparing fresh carrot juice for soup bases and also is needed to make several of the high-nutrient vegetable juices.

Cooking techniques

WATER SAUTÉING

The first basic technique you will learn is water sautéing (also called sweating or steam frying). This is used instead of cooking with oil. Water sautéing is simple and useful for stir-fries, sauces, and many other dishes. To water sauté, heat a skillet on high heat until water sputters when dropped on the pan. Use small amounts of water in the hot skillet, wok, or pan, covering occasionally, and adding more water when necessary until the vegetables are tender. Do not add too much water, or the food will be boiled, not sautéed.

HELPFUL HINT:

Eating too quickly encourages overeating and can tax the digestive system. It takes about 15 minutes for your brain to realize that your stomach is full. If you eat too fast, your body won't have enough time to tell you when it's full. You will end up eating more than you really needed. Slow down, thoroughly chew your food, and enjoy the experience of eating. Don't just grab food without thinking about it.

Soups and stews are critical components of this eating style. When vegetables are simmered in soup, all the nutrients are retained in the liquid. Soups and stews are cooked at 212° F, the boiling point of water. Cooking at this low temperature is very healthful because acrylamides are not produced. Acrylamides are the cancer-causing agents formed when foods are fried, baked, roasted, or grilled.

Many of the soup recipes use fresh vegetable juices, especially carrot juice. My *Famous Anti-Cancer Soup* utilizes both carrot juice and celery juice to provide a great tasting, antioxidant-rich base. If you don't have a juicer, you should consider purchasing one. If you are short of time, bottled carrot and other vegetable juices can be purchased at most health food stores, but don't expect them to taste as good as freshly squeezed. Low-sodium V8 juice is another option to add to the soup base.

To make a "cream" soup, like my *Golden Austrian Cauliflower Soup*, raw cashews or cashew butter can be blended into the soup to provide a creamy texture and rich flavor. In many of my recipes, a portion of the cooked soup is removed from the pot and blended with raw cashews. This blended portion is then added back to the pot.

A big advantage to making soups and stews is that they make great leftovers. Soups generally keep well for up to five days in the refrigerator, but should be frozen if longer storage is desired. Be creative with your soup-making. Once you get the general idea, you can mix and match ingredients. Start with a base such as carrot juice, tomato juice, or organic low-sodium packaged broth. Add some leafy greens, a member of the onion family, a no-salt seasoning mix like my VegiZest or MatoZest, and any other vegetables that you have on hand. Don't forget the beans! Create new soups by matching up different items from the columns in the chart on the following page.

SOUPS AND STEWS—THE HIGH-NUTRIENT WAY					
BASE	LEAFY GREENS	ONION FAMILY	VEGETABLES	FLAVOR	BEANS
carrot juice	kale	onion	tomato, fresh/canned	VegiZest Seasoning Mix*	adzuki
low-sodium vegetable broth	spinach	leek	zucchini	sun-dried tomato	red kidney
tomato juice	cabbage	garlic	red/green pepper	bay leaf	split peas
celery juice	Swiss chard	ginger	celery	cilantro/ parsley	black beans
low-sodium V-8	bok choy	shallots	parsnips	chili powder/ cumin	garbanzos
beet juice	collards	scallions	carrots	curry powder	lentils
			celery root	lemon	navy beans
			mushrooms	hot pepper	

*available at www.DrFuhrman.com

HELPFUL HINT:

If you occasionally use a prepared soup, keep in mind that your overall daily sodium intake should be under 1200 mg and preferably under 1000 mg. Since you get 400-700 mg of sodium daily from natural whole foods, you don't want prepared soups to push you over the limit. Be sure to read the labels; you will be amazed at how much sodium canned soup contains.

SALAD DRESSINGS

The high-nutrient diet is not a fat-free program because we need to eat healthful fats the way nature intended us to—in whole natural foods. You can eat delicious creamy nut sauces and dressings made with nuts, seeds, and avocados. By eating this way, you get the lignins, flavonoids, antioxidants, minerals, and other protective phytochemicals that come along in the package. Seeds and nuts become disease-prevention foods.

Salad Dressings and dips usually start with oil and vinegar; the oil provides the fat, and the vinegar provides the acidity. Instead of highly processed oils, my Salad Dressings use whole foods as fat sources—almonds and cashews, other nuts and seeds, avocado, and tahini. These healthful fat sources are blended together in a high-powered blender or food processor with other ingredients to create delicious creamy dressings and dips that you can feel good about eating.

Some popular dressings and dips featured in the recipe section of this book are *Cashew Caesar, Dijon Pistachio,* and *Russian Fig.* My gourmet fruit-flavored vinegars are used in many recipes because they add unique and delicious flavors. Garlic, onions, fruit, Dijon mustard, and herbs and spices contribute additional character and interest. Items from this chart can be combined to create new flavors while maintaining the health quality of the dressings.

SALAD DRESSINGS—THE HIGH-NUTRIENT WAY			
FLAVOR	**FAT**	**ACIDITY**	**OTHER**
garlic	raw almonds or almond butter	balsamic vinegar	tofu
onion	raw cashews or cashew butter	Spicy Pecan Vinegar*	soy, almond, or hemp milk
fresh/dried herbs	pecans	Blood Orange Vinegar*	juice
spices (no salt)	pistachios	Black Fig Vinegar*	tomato sauce
Dijon mustard	tahini and sesame seeds	Riesling Raisin Vinegar*	fruit preserves
nutritional yeast	pumpkin/ sunflower seeds	D'Anjou Pear Vinegar*	fresh or dried fruit
VegiZest*	avocado	lemon juice	frozen berries

*available at www.DrFuhrman.com

SMOOTHIES AND BLENDED SALADS

Blending raw vegetables with fruit is an efficient way to increase your nutrient absorption. All plants are composed of cells whose walls consist mainly of cellulose, a type of carbohydrate. Humans do not have the enzyme capable of breaking down cellulose, so we cannot utilize cellulose as an energy source. The only way we can break down these walls and release the most nutrients possible from the cells into the bloodstream is by thoroughly chewing fruits and vegetables.

However, when we chew a salad, we often don't do an efficient job of crushing every cell; about 70-90 percent of the cells are not broken open. As a result, most of the valuable nutrients contained within those cells never enter our bloodstream and are lost. They just travel through our bodies until they are excreted. This is one of the reasons why chewing is so important.

An even more efficient way to ensure that you receive these needed nutrients is to use a blender to purée raw, leafy greens. A high-powered blender like the Vita-Mix brand is essential for making these smoothies and blended salads. The blending process aids your body in the work of breaking down and assimilating nutrients. It guarantees that a higher percentage of nutrients will be absorbed into your bloodstream. In addition, some people have difficulty digesting large quantities of roughage when they first switch to a natural, plant-based diet. Often, problems with gas and bloating can be solved by replacing some whole, raw, and cooked fruits and vegetables with blended dishes and juices. Making green smoothies or blended salads is a delicious and convenient way to pump up your consumption of greens.

While you sip or eat a creamy-smooth blended salad, think about all of the nutrients that are now powering your body to restore and maintain optimal health. Savory blended salads can be made with endless combinations of vegetables, nuts, herbs, and condiments. They can be made to taste like gazpacho, creamy summer soups, fruit shakes, or salad dressings. My typical green smoothie blends two ounces of lettuce, two ounces of spinach, a banana, a date, and half an avocado.

You will find several delicious green smoothies (blended salads) among my recipes. The *Chocolate Cherry Smoothie,* for example, blends fresh spinach with banana, cherries, and pomegranate juice. The *Blended Mango Smoothie* is a delicious combination of mango blended with romaine lettuce and spinach. There are infinite blending combinations. In our menus and recipes, we give you several options and encourage you to make your own combinations of anything from creamy cold vegetable soups to pudding-like desserts. Start with some greens, like spinach, kale, romaine or avocado. Add in some fresh or frozen fruit, such as blueberries, strawberries, oranges, banana, pineapple, or kiwi. You also can add other flavors and liquids according to your taste preferences. This chart will help you come up with new possibilities.

SMOOTHIES—THE HIGH-NUTRIENT WAY			
LIQUID (OPTIONAL)	GREENS	FRUIT (FRESH OR FROZEN)	FLAVOR/OTHER
almond, hemp, or soy milk	spinach	blueberries	dates
pomegranate juice	avocado	strawberries	flax, hemp, and chia seeds
orange juice	kale	oranges	Goji berries
other fruit juices	lettuce	banana	cocoa powder, natural
	collards	pineapple	nuts
		kiwi	unsweetened coconut

JUICING

In addition to blending, I also recommend nutrient-dense juices like my *Mixed Vegetable Juice* and the *High Cruciferous Juice*. With juicing, you retain many of the phytochemicals and other nutrients but lose other beneficial components like fiber and proteins. Juicing should not replace the fruits or vegetables in your diet, but it is an effective way to boost your nutrient absorption because you can easily consume a lot of nutrients from raw green vegetables.

Juicing is different from blending. Blending incorporates the entire food into the mixture, whereas juicing extracts the liquid but leaves the pulp behind. Two different appliances are used. Smoothies and blended salads are made with a blender while a juicer is needed to make juice. If you add a glass of freshly squeezed vegetable juice to your diet periodically, you will pump up your vegetable consumption and increase the availability and absorption of the anticancer phytochemical compounds.

If you have a digestive disorder, blending and juicing vegetables can be a great aid because you can increase your consumption of healing nutrients, even though your digestive capacity might be sub-par. Fortunately, eating a high-nutrient, vegetable-based diet often quickly resolves the digestive problems caused by eating a low-phytochemical, low-fiber diet. People suffering from irritable bowel syndrome, constipation, hemorrhoids, and reflux disease often see improvements after just a few weeks of juicing and eating blended salads. However, sometimes diets have to be modified for individual conditions or medical problems, such as ulcerative colitis or Crohn's disease, conditions that require fresh fruits and raw vegetables to be gradually introduced into the diet. In such cases, working with a knowledgeable physician may be helpful.

The high-nutrient availability of blended vegetables also helps normalize immune function in those suffering from asthma, allergies, and other immune system disorders. High-performance athletes or those interested in gaining weight can mix nuts and seeds into their blended vegetables. This combination supplies healthful sources of protein and fat in an efficiently absorbed, high-nutrient package.

Quick and easy meal suggestions

The cooking instructions here are intended to encourage you to branch out with your own creative recipes. Many people who follow these guidelines share delightful high-nutrient recipes on my website (www.DrFuhrman.com). However, this way of eating does not require any complicated food preparation. In fact, you may spend far less time in the kitchen than before.

It is so easy to just shred some romaine lettuce and drizzle some tahini and lemon juice over it, heat up a tasty vegetable stew, or make a green smoothie. One of the most enjoyable results of eating this way is that even simple foods will taste better.

Don't forget to make creative use of leftovers. You do not need to cook every day. Plan to cook a healthful, nutrient-dense soup or stew two times a week. The leftovers can be used for lunch or dinners in the days that follow. The same can be done with dips and salad dressings.

You do not have to use fancy recipes all the time. Simple foods are quick and easy and can work in this program, too. Consider some of the following options to make your diet easier and more convenient.

BREAKFAST

Combine fresh fruit in season or even frozen fruit with raw nuts and seeds, or have old-fashioned or steel-cut oatmeal, with cut-up fruit on top. You also could make a quick smoothie with fruit and flaxseed, or have a hearty, whole grain bread, like Alvarado Street, Manna Bread, or Ezekiel brands, with a trans-fat free spread or raw almond or cashew butter.

LUNCH AND DINNER

Your basic lunch should be a salad with a healthful dressing and a bowl of vegetable or bean soup that you made on the weekend. Make a quick salad from pre-mixed and pre-washed greens. Add chopped nuts, cut up fresh fruit, or low-sodium canned beans, and use a low-fat and low-sodium dressing or dip, fresh lemon, or balsamic or other flavored vinegar. You also can eat raw vegetables and avocado with low-sodium salsa or hummus dip, or a low-sodium/low-fat store-bought dressing.

Having some defrosted frozen vegetables or fresh or frozen fruit is a good way to round out a meal, salad, or leftover dish. Try steaming some fresh broccoli, spinach, or another green vegetable and adding a flavoring like VegiZest. Add just a pinch of olive oil to raw vegetables such as broccoli, and then add chopped garlic and onion. Easy options that are popular with children are baked sweet potato or corn on the cob served with a trans-fat free spread or no-salt vegetable seasoning. A quick and tasty stir-fry using the water sauté method can be made from whatever fresh vegetables you have on hand.

Another easy meal option is to stuff whole wheat pita bread or a whole wheat wrap with shredded romaine or other greens, tomato, sun-dried tomatoes (pre-soaked in water), cucumber, bean sprouts, broccoli slaw, or cole slaw mix. You can add hummus, avocado, salsa, tahini, or nut butter. I often mash almond butter and tomato sauce together with Black Fig Vinegar and put it in the pita with tomatoes, avocado, and shredded lettuce. Many families enjoy whole grain lentil pasta with lots of vegetables and a good low-sodium tomato sauce.

HELPFUL HINT:

In addition to adding great flavor to all kinds of dishes, onions and mushrooms have well-documented cancer-protective properties. Onions and their allium family members contain chemo-protective organosulfur compounds[3], and consuming mushrooms regularly has been shown to decrease risk of breast cancer by over 60 percent[4]. Add them to soups, stews, stir-fries, and other vegetable recipes.

3. Powolny AA, Singh SV. "Multitargeted prevention and therapy of cancer by diallyl trisulfide and related Allium vegetable-derived organosulfur compounds." *Cancer Lett* 2008 Oct 8;269(2):305-314.

4. Zhang M, et al. "Dietary intakes of mushrooms and green tea combine to reduce the risk of breast cancer in Chinese women." *Int J Cancer* 2009;124:1404-1408.

THREE LEVELS OF SUPERIOR NUTRITION

I have organized the following menu plans into three levels of superior nutrition. Based on your health needs and current dietary habits, you can choose between three different diet options, starting on Level 1 and working your way up to Level 3. I would like to see everyone reach at least Level 2, although for many, even Level 1 would represent a significant improvement.

Over time, your taste and food preferences change. You become more comfortable eating high-nutrient foods, and it will become second nature—the way you prefer to eat. This is a high-nutrient program, not a calorie-counting one. Keep your focus on increasing your intake of disease-protective nutrients by eating whole natural foods. Use *Dr. Fuhrman's Nutrient Density Scores* to help you choose the most nutrient-dense foods. When you eat foods that have very high scores, you will be satisfied with fewer calories and will no longer be driven to overeat.

Following this chapter, you will find four weeks of menus that can be adapted to the level of superior nutrition you wish to achieve. You can pick one level and stick with it, but the menus are set up to give you the flexibility on a daily basis to decide between Levels 1, 2, and 3. I have included my favorite recipes in these menus. High-nutrient density soups, delicious fruit smoothies, and dressings and dips are featured in all my meal plans.

I have designed most of the recipes to be at least at Level 2 to ensure that most people get the level of superior nutrition they need for their individual health conditions. This does not mean you shouldn't move to Level 3 if you are comfortable doing so, or down to Level 1 if you don't have pressing health concerns. In the menus, I provide Level 1, 2 and 3 meals for all 4 weeks. Some meals are the same for all levels, while other meals use different recipes or modified ingredients depending on the level. This provides a starting place for everyone

For all levels, follow these high-nutrient guidelines.

INCLUDE DAILY:

1) a large salad

2) at least a half-cup serving of beans/legumes in soup, salad, or some other dish

3) at least three fresh fruits

4) at least one ounce of raw nuts and seeds

5) at least one large (double-sized) serving of steamed green vegetables

AVOID:

1) barbequed, processed, and cured meats and red meat

2) fried foods

3) full-fat dairy (cheese, ice cream, butter, whole milk, and two percent milk), and trans fat (margarine)

4) soft drinks, sugar, and artificial sweeteners

5) white flour products

LEVEL 1

Level 1 is appropriate for a person who is healthy, thin, physically fit, and exercises regularly. You should have no risk factors such as high blood pressure, high cholesterol, or a family history of heart disease, stroke, or cancer before age 75.

Most Americans do have risk factors or a family history of strokes, heart attacks, and cancer, and most Americans are overweight. So most people should only see Level 1 as a temporary stage as they learn about high-nutrient eating and allow their taste buds to acclimate to whole, natural plant foods.

Level 1 is designed to ease the emotional shock of making profound dietary improvements. It enables people to revamp their diet at a level that is significant, but not overwhelming. Enjoy this new style of eating, allow your taste preferences to change with time, and learn some great recipes. You soon may decide to move up to a higher level. However, I still recommend that the majority of individuals make the commitment to jump right into the more nutrient-dense Levels 2 and 3 because so many people are significantly overweight and have risk factors that need to be addressed immediately. People in desperate need of a health makeover need to start on Levels 2 or 3.

On Level 1, you eliminate fried foods and substitute fruit-based healthful desserts and whole grains for low-nutrient processed snack foods such as salty snacks, candy, ice cream, and baked products. Whole grain products like old-fashioned oats, wild rice, brown rice, 100 percent whole grain bread, and pasta made with 100 percent whole grain or bean flour are used. Bread and pasta made with white flour are eliminated.

Your sodium intake will decrease as you begin to make these dietary changes. Processed foods and restaurant foods contribute 77 percent of the sodium people consume. Salt from the saltshaker provides 11 percent, and sodium found naturally in food provides the remaining 12 percent.

You also eliminate foods like cheese and butter that are high in saturated fats. Your cooking techniques use only a minimal amount of oil. Most Americans consume over 15 servings of animal products weekly. On Level 1, I recommend only four servings of animal products per week. These animal products are limited to fish, chicken, turkey, eggs, or nonfat dairy products.

LEVEL 2

Level 2 builds on the positive changes described for Level 1. On Level 2, animal products are reduced to three servings weekly, and vegetables and beans make up an even larger portion of your total caloric intake. When you incorporate more and more nutrient-rich produce in your diet, you automatically increase your intake of antioxidants, phytochemicals, plant fibers, lignins, and plant sterols. You lower the glycemic index of your diet and the level of saturated fat, salt, and other negative elements without having to think about it. Your ability to appreciate the natural flavors of unprocessed, whole foods will improve with time because you lose your dependence on salt and sugar. Add more beans and nuts to your diet to replace animal products. Try some of my high-nutrient dressing and dip recipes. They use heart-healthy nuts to replace the oils found in traditional dressings and dips.

Level 2 is a reasonable target diet for most people. If you want to lose weight, lower your cholesterol, lower your blood pressure, or just live a long and healthy life, this is the level you should adopt.

LEVEL 3

If you suffer from serious medical conditions like diabetes, heart disease, or autoimmune disease, or just want to optimize the nutrient density of your diet to slow aging and maximize longevity, step up to Level 3, where superior nutrition hits its peak. If you suffer from a medical condition that is important to reverse, this is the right prescription for you. If you are on medications and you want to be able to discontinue them as quickly as possible, go for Level 3. It is also the level to choose if you have trouble losing weight, no matter what you do, and want to maximize your results. Level 3 is designed for those who want to reverse serious disease or for healthy people who want to push the envelope of human longevity.

Level 3 is the diet that I use in my medical practice for people who have serious autoimmune diseases (such as rheumatoid arthritis or lupus), or when someone has life-threatening heart disease (athero-sclerosis). I prescribe it for diabetics who need to lower their blood sugars into the normal range, or to get rid of severe migraines. It delivers the highest level of nutrient density.

Level 3 includes just two or fewer servings of animal products weekly and concentrates on high-nutrient-density vegetables. Use *Dr. Fuhrman's Nutrient Density Scores* to select the most nutrient-dense foods possible. Use green smoothies, fresh vegetable juices, healthful soups, and lots of greens and raw vegetables to make every calorie count.

At this level, you should consume processed foods only rarely. Keep the use of refined fats and oils to a minimum. Nuts and seeds supply essential fats in a much healthier package, with significant health benefits. Use the recipes in this book to incorporate a variety of nutrient-dense foods into your diet.

Eating in sufficient quantities

Eating enough healthful food is critical to your success. You will find that when you eat enough high-nutrient food, you no longer desire or even have room for the foods you used to eat. Processed and refined foods offer little in terms of nutrients and phytochemicals. When you eat them, you are losing out on a great many valuable nutrients that your body needs.

LEVEL 1

Animal products .... 4 servings/week or less

Whole grain products* and starchy vegetables**............ 4 servings/day or less

Sodium*** .... 1600 mg/day

Fats/oils.................... 1 Tbsp. of olive oil or replaceable substitute**** per day

Beverage .... water, fresh-squeezed juice, herbal teas,
1 cup coffee/tea, if desired

IMPORTANT GOALS

- Increase consumption of nutrient-dense vegetables and fruit.

- Reduce sodium consumption.

- Continually reduce consumption of refined foods, animal products, and sodium.

LEVEL 2

Animal products .... 3 servings/week or less

Whole grain products* and starchy vegetables**............ 3 servings/day or less

Sodium*** .... 1200 mg/day

Fats/oils.................... 1 Tbsp. of olive oil or replaceable substitute**** per day

Beverage .... water, fresh-squeezed juice, herbal teas,
1 cup coffee/tea, if desired

IMPORTANT GOALS

- Reduce consumption of processed and refined foods.

- Increase consumption of beans and nuts.

- Begin to eliminate oil and caffeine.

LEVEL 3

Animal products .... 2 servings/week or less

Whole grain products* and starchy vegetables**............ 2 servings/day or less

Sodium*** .... 900 mg/day

Fats/oils..Minimal

Beverage ....water, fresh-squeezed juice, herbal tea, vegetable juices

> **IMPORTANT GOALS**
>
> - Reduce consumption of animal products.
> - Increase consumption of green vegetables.
> - Maximize nutrient density and absorption.

    * Only use whole grains: cooked and dry cereals, bread, tortillas, pasta, and brown rice.

  ** Starchy vegetables include corn, white potatoes, sweet potatoes, squash, carrots, and parsnips.

*** The amount of sodium allotted includes that which is naturally occurring in foods (approximately 700 mg), plus what is added.

**** Substitutes include non-dairy spreads without trans-fats and hydrogenated oil such as Earth Balance, Smart Balance, and Spectrum.

Practice makes perfect

As you now know from reading so far, the most effective way to properly care for your health is to strive for superior nutrition. To do that, you must stay focused on the nutrient quality of the food you eat. However, I want to reiterate, this program doesn't demand perfection, nor does it mean that you will never eat meat again or that you will never have a slice of birthday cake. It means that your diet has been revamped so that high-nutrient fruits, vegetables, beans, and other foods make up the large majority of your food intake, and that you have the knowledge and skills to come even closer to superior nutrition each day. The instances when you eat meat and cakes will be fewer, but you will undoubtedly find that, with time, those foods are less enjoyable. You may eventually choose not to eat them or other unhealthful foods because you have lost your desire and taste for them and have found healthier options that you enjoy more.

What you have read in this book has shown you that there is a whole body of nutritional information that has never been shared with the general public. Even with highly educated health professionals, the power of lifestyle intervention and dietary modifications is hardly addressed because the emphasis is on intervention with pills, drugs, and surgeries. Commercial interests have dominated the nutritional message we have learned to date, and the medical profession has become infatuated with technological advancements. This approach has not only failed to improve the general health of our nation, but it has also resulted in a dramatic explosion of the diseases of nutritional ignorance and pushed health-care spending through the roof without any improvement in healthy life expectancy to show for it.

I hope that you will use the strength of superior nutrition to achieve enhanced vigor and incredible health. Protecting yourself from needless medical tragedy is not only in your best interest, but is a gratifying experience that can bring satisfaction and pleasure to your life. Your success will encourage others to get healthy, too. Perhaps from your example, others will discover how rewarding it is to eat healthfully. The power of the high-nutrient diet is knowledge that we all deserve so that we can make critical choices for our own lives and take back control of our health.

CONGRATULATIONS FOR EMBARKING ON YOUR JOURNEY
TOWARD INCREDIBLE HEALTH.

4

FOUR-WEEK MENU PLANS

The following menus provide 1400 calories daily. For most people, this will result in moderate weight loss. If you do not need to lose weight, you can include some of the options listed at the bottom of each day's menu or include a more generous amount of raw nuts and seeds in your diet. Because this is not a calorie-counting diet, you can eat as much as you desire. When you eat a micronutrient rich diet, you naturally desire fewer calories. Eat when you are hungry. If you are not hungry, don't eat. Everyone has different caloric needs, so you may require more or fewer calories than suggested in these menus.

I consider the Level 2 menus to be a good starting point. You can use the tips and suggestions throughout this book to personalize your meals, adjusting the level of superior nutrition up or down to match your goals and health needs. If at a particular meal you want to move up or down a level, it is fine to do so.

WEEK 1

DAY ONE

	LEVEL 1	LEVEL 2	LEVEL 3
BREAKFAST	sprouted-grain bread with fat-free spread; melon or other fresh fruit	Wild Blueberry Hot Breakfast*	Wild Blueberry Hot Breakfast*
LUNCH	raw veggies; whole wheat pita with Tasty Hummus*, mixed greens, tomato, and chopped red pepper; grapes or other fresh fruit	raw veggies; whole wheat pita with Tasty Hummus*, mixed greens, tomato, and chopped red pepper; grapes or other fresh fruit	raw veggies; broccoli with Red Lentil Sauce* topped with pecans; grapes or other fresh fruit
DINNER	mixed greens and assorted vegetables; Ten Thousand Island Dressing*; Golden Austrian Cauliflower Soup*; Peach Sorbet*	mixed greens and assorted vegetables; Ten Thousand Island Dressing*; Golden Austrian Cauliflower Soup*; Peach Sorbet*	mixed greens and assorted vegetables topped with bean or broccoli sprouts; Ten Thousand Island Dressing*; Golden Austrian Cauliflower Soup*; Peach Sorbet*

options for higher calorie diets:

   LUNCH – add sliced avocado

   DINNER – add Sweet Potato and Asparagus Ragout*

DAY TWO

	LEVEL 1	LEVEL 2	LEVEL 3
BREAKFAST	Fruit and Nut Bowl*	Fruit and Nut Bowl*	Fruit and Nut Bowl*
LUNCH	mixed greens and arugula salad; low-fat/low-sodium purchased dressing; Easy Vegetable Pizza*; pear or other fresh fruit	mixed greens and arugula salad; Russian Fig Dressing/Dip*; French Minted Pea Soup*; pear or other fresh fruit	mixed greens and arugula salad; Russian Fig Dressing/Dip*; French Minted Pea Soup*; pear or other fresh fruit
DINNER	raw veggies; low-fat/low-sodium dressing/dip; Orange Kale-Choy and Chicken* (vegan option: Super Lentil Loaf*); brown rice	raw veggies; Russian Fig Dressing/Dip*; Orange Kale-Choy and Chicken* (vegan option: Super Lentil Loaf*); brown and wild rice	raw veggies; Russian Fig Dressing/Dip*; Super Lentil Loaf*; Kale with Cashew Cream Sauce*

options for higher-calorie diets
BREAKFAST
OR DESSERT – Yummy Banana Oat Bars*

WEEK 1

DAY THREE

LEVEL 1	LEVEL 2	LEVEL 3
BREAKFAST whole grain cereal with soy, hemp, or almond milk sprinkled with ground flaxseed; banana or other fresh fruit	Cinnamon Fruit Oatmeal*	Cinnamon Fruit Oatmeal*
LUNCH raw vegetables; Zesty Avocado Dressing/Dip*; Vegetable Bean Burrito*; apple or other fresh fruit	raw vegetables; Zesty Avocado Dressing/Dip*; Vegetable Bean Burrito*; apple or other fresh fruit	raw vegetables; Zesty Avocado Dressing/Dip*; Southern Style Mixed Salad*; apple or other fresh fruit
DINNER romaine salad with assorted vegetables; Zesty Avocado Dressing/Dip*; "Cheesy" Kale Soup*; Acorn Squash Supreme*	romaine salad with assorted vegetables; Zesty Avocado Dressing/Dip*; "Cheesy" Kale Soup*; Acorn Squash Supreme*	romaine salad with assorted vegetables; Zesty Avocado Dressing/Dip*; "Cheesy" Kale Soup*; Swiss Chard with Garlic and Lemon*

options for higher-calorie diets

LUNCH – add two tablespoons to nondairy cheese to Vegetable Bean Burrito*

add pecans to Southern Style Mixed Salad*

add raw cashew or almond butter to apple slices

DAY FOUR

	LEVEL 1	LEVEL 2	LEVEL 3
BREAKFAST	Blueberry Orange Smoothie*	Blueberry Orange Smoothie*	Super-Easy Blended Salad*
LUNCH	Spinach and Garbanzo Bean Salad with Lemon Fig Dressing*; pineapple or other fresh fruit	Spinach and Garbanzo Bean Salad with Lemon Fig Dressing*; pineapple or other fresh fruit	Spinach and Garbanzo Bean Salad with Lemon Fig Dressing*; pineapple or other fresh fruit
DINNER	Black Bean and Corn Salsa* with low-sodium tortilla chips*; Turkey Spinach Burger* (vegan option: Better Burgers*) on whole grain bun with lettuce, tomato, and chopped onion; Sweet Potato Fries*; strawberries dusted with cocoa powder	Black Bean and Corn Salsa* with endive spears; Better Burgers* on whole grain bun with lettuce, tomato, and chopped onion; Broccoli Fra Diavolo*; strawberries dusted with cocoa powder	Asparagus Shiitake Salad with Creamy Sesame Dressing/ Dip*; Broccoli Fra Diavolo*; strawberries dusted with cocoa powder

options for higher-calorie diets

> **DINNER** – avocado slices on burger or salad
> **DESSERT** – Chocolate Dip* for strawberries

DAY FIVE

	LEVEL 1	LEVEL 2	LEVEL 3
BREAKFAST	Cinnamon Fruit Oatmeal*; fresh orange juice	Cinnamon Fruit Oatmeal*; fresh orange juice	Cinnamon Fruit Oatmeal*; Mixed Vegetable Juice*
LUNCH	whole wheat pita with avocado slices, shredded lettuce, sliced tomato, and chopped cucumber; berries or other fresh fruit	Arugula and Spinach Stuffed Pitas with Watercress Pesto*; berries or other fresh fruit	steamed vegetables with Sesame Ginger Sauce*; berries or other fresh fruit
DINNER	Pom Salad with Figs and Pumpkin Seeds*; Chunky Sweet Potato Stew*	Pom Salad with Figs and Pumpkin Seeds*; Tuscan Greens and Beans Soup*	Pom Salad with Figs and Pumpkin Seeds*; Tuscan Greens and Beans Soup*

options for higher-calorie diets

DESSERT – Blueberry Banana Cobbler*

WEEK 1

DAY SIX

	LEVEL 1	LEVEL 2	LEVEL 3
BREAKFAST	Healthy Pancakes*; Fruit and Berry Compote*	Fruit and Nut Bowl*	Fruit and Nut Bowl*
LUNCH	turkey sandwich on whole grain bread with mixed greens and tomato; melon or other fresh fruit	Tuscan Greens and Beans Soup* (leftover); melon or other fresh fruit	Tuscan Greens and Beans Soup* (leftover); melon or other fresh fruit
DINNER	romaine salad; purchased low-fat/low-sodium dressing; Salmon and Vegetables in a Packet* with brown rice (vegan option: Tofu with Pumpkin Seed Coating* with Great Greens*); Banana Fig "Ice Cream"*	romaine salad; Cashew Caesar Dressing*; Salmon and Vegetables in a Packet*; brown and wild rice (vegan option: Tofu with Pumpkin Seed Coating* with Great Greens*); Banana Fig "Ice Cream"*	romaine salad; Cashew Caesar Dressing*; Salmon and Vegetables in a Packet* served over baby greens (vegan option: Tofu with Pumpkin Seed Coating* with Great Greens*); Banana Fig "Ice Cream"*

options for higher-calorie diets
> **BREAKFAST** – add unsulfured dried fruit (figs, apricots, currents) to Fruit and Nut Bowl* or Fruit and Berry Compote*

DAY SEVEN

	LEVEL 1	LEVEL 2	LEVEL 3
BREAKFAST	Scrambled Veggies and Eggs* (vegan option: Deluxe Scrambled Tofu*); mango or other fresh fruit	Scrambled Veggies and Eggs* (vegan option: Deluxe Scrambled Tofu*); mango or other fresh fruit	Scrambled Veggies and Eggs* (vegan option: Deluxe Scrambled Tofu*); mango or other fresh fruit
LUNCH	raw veggies; Portobello and Red Pepper Sandwich*	raw veggies; Portobello and Red Pepper Sandwich*	raw veggies; Apple Cinnamon Butternut Squash Soup*
DINNER	mixed greens with assorted vegetables; choice of Dr. Fuhrman's healthful salad dressings; Spaghetti Squash Primavera*; berries or other fresh fruit	Arugula Salad with Sun-Dried Tomato Dressing*; Spaghetti Squash Primavera*; berries or other fresh fruit	Arugula Salad with Sun-Dried Tomato Dressing*; Spaghetti Squash Primavera*; Lemon Zest Spinach*; berries or other fresh fruit

options for higher-calorie diets

> **BREAKFAST** – whole grain toast with 100 percent fruit spread
>
> **DINNER** – add pine nuts to salad
>
> **DESSERT** – Summer Fruit Pie*

DAY ONE

	LEVEL 1	LEVEL 2	LEVEL 3
BREAKFAST	Apple Pie Smoothie*	Raspberry Frosty Blended Salad*	Raspberry Frosty Blended Salad*
LUNCH	baby greens and watercress with chopped walnuts; Russian Fig Dressing/ Dip*; kiwis or other fruit	baby greens and watercress with chopped walnuts; Russian Fig Dressing/ Dip*; kiwis or other fruit	Nutra-Green Salad with Black Fig Dressing*; kiwis or other fruit
DINNER	baked whole grain tortilla triangles; Simple Guacamole*; Easy Three-Bean Vegetable Chili*; brown rice	raw vegetables; Simple Guacamole*; Easy Three-Bean Vegetable Chili*; brown and wild rice	raw vegetables; Simple Guacamole*; Easy Three-Bean Vegetable Chili*; Supreme Kale*

options for higher-calorie diets

    LUNCH – top salad with beans

    DESSERT – Red Velvet Sorbet*

WEEK 2

DAY TWO

LEVEL 1	LEVEL 2	LEVEL 3
BREAKFAST whole grain bagel with 100 percent fruit spread	Special Oatmeal*	Special Oatmeal*
LUNCH raw vegetables; Tuscan White Bean Dip*; Easy Three-Bean Vegetable Chili* (leftover); orange or other fresh fruit	raw vegetables; Tuscan White Bean Dip*; Easy Three-Bean Vegetable Chili* (leftover); orange or other fresh fruit	raw vegetables; Tuscan White Bean Dip*; Easy Three-Bean Vegetable Chili* (leftover); orange or other fresh fruit
DINNER edamame with no-salt seasoning; Kale Pesto over Pasta and Beans*	edamame with no-salt seasoning; Kale Pesto over Pasta and Beans*	edamame with no-salt seasoning; Braised Kale and Squash with Pumpkin Seeds*

options for higher-calorie diets

    BREAKFAST – 100 percent fruit juice

    DESSERT – Apple Surprise*

DAY THREE

	LEVEL 1	LEVEL 2	LEVEL 3
BREAKFAST	whole grain cereal with soy, hemp, or almond milk with ground flaxseed; berries or other fresh fruit	Tropical Fruit Salad*	Tropical Fruit Salad*; Sunrise Juice*
LUNCH	raw vegetables; purchased low-fat/low-sodium dressing; Black Bean Lettuce Bundles*; watermelon or other fresh fruit	raw vegetables; Tomato Garlic Dressing*; Black Bean Lettuce Bundles*; watermelon or other fresh fruit	raw vegetables; Tomato Garlic Dressing*; Black Bean Lettuce Bundles*; watermelon or other fresh fruit
DINNER	mixed greens, romaine, and assorted vegetables; purchased low-fat/low-sodium dressing; Black Forest Cream of Mushroom Soup*; Easy Ratatouille*	mixed greens, romaine, and assorted vegetables; Tomato Garlic Dressing*; Black Forest Cream of Mushroom Soup*; Easy Ratatouille*	mixed greens, romaine, and assorted vegetables; Tomato Garlic Dressing*; Black Forest Cream of Mushroom Soup*; Brussels Sprouts Polonaise*

options for higher-calorie diets

BREAKFAST – add raw nuts or seeds

LUNCH – sliced avocado

DESSERT – Mixed Berry Freeze*

DAY FOUR

	LEVEL 1	LEVEL 2	LEVEL 3
BREAKFAST	Honeydew Berry Smoothie*	Honeydew Berry Smoothie*	Antioxidant-Rich Smoothie*
LUNCH	Speedy Vegetable Wrap*; cherries or other fruit	Black Forest Cream of Mushroom Soup* (leftover); cherries or other fruit	Black Forest Cream of Mushroom Soup* (leftover); cherries or other fruit
DINNER	Waldorf-ish Salad*; Turkey Vegetable Meatloaf* (vegan option: Garden Stuffed Vegetables*); baked potato with trans-free spread and no-salt seasoning; Lemon Zest Spinach*	Waldorf-ish Salad*; Turkey Vegetable Meatloaf* (vegan option: Garden Stuffed Vegetables*); Cauliflower Spinach Mashed Potatoes*; Lemon Zest Spinach*	Waldorf-ish Salad*; Garden Stuffed Vegetables*; Lemon Zest Spinach*

options for higher-calorie diets

BREAKFAST – unsulfured dried apricots or figs
Banana Cashew Lettuce Wrap*

DAY FIVE

	LEVEL 1	LEVEL 2	LEVEL 3
BREAKFAST	Quick Banana Berry Breakfast To Go*	Quick Banana Berry Breakfast To Go*	Quick Banana Berry Breakfast To Go*
LUNCH	turkey on sprouted wheat bread with mixed greens, broccoli sprouts, and tomato with mustard; pear or other fresh fruit	Eggplant Hummus* and avocado slices on sprouted wheat bread with mixed greens, broccoli sprouts and tomato; pear or other fresh fruit	Black Bean Lettuce Bundles*; pear or other fresh fruit
DINNER	mixed greens and watercress salad; Dijon Pistachio Dressing/Dip*; Swiss Chard and Sweet Potato Gratin*; steamed broccoli	mixed greens and watercress salad; Dijon Pistachio Dressing/Dip*; Swiss Chard and Sweet Potato Gratin*; steamed broccoli	mixed greens and watercress salad; Dijon Pistachio Dressing/Dip*; Swiss Chard and Sweet Potato Gratin*; steamed broccoli

options for higher-calorie diets

DESSERT – Wild Apple Crunch*

WEEK 2

DAY SIX

	LEVEL 1	LEVEL 2	LEVEL 3
BREAKFAST	whole grain bagel with trans-fat-free spread; melon or other fresh fruit	Fruit and Nut Bowl*	Fruit and Nut Bowl*
LUNCH	Speedy Vegetable Wrap*; berries or other fresh fruit	Speedy Vegetable Wrap*; berries or other fresh fruit	mixed greens, watercress, and assorted vegetables; Orange Peanut Dressing/Dip*; berries or other fruit
DINNER	raw vegetables; Island Black Bean Dip*; Creamy Broccoli Lentil Soup*; Chocolate Cherry "Ice Cream"*	raw vegetables; Island Black Bean Dip*; Creamy Broccoli Lentil Soup*; Chocolate Cherry "Ice Cream"*	raw vegetables; Island Black Bean Dip*; Creamy Broccoli Lentil Soup*; Chocolate Cherry "Ice Cream"*

options for higher-calorie diets

BREAKFAST – unsulfured dried fruit

LUNCH – apple slices with raw almond or cashew butter

DAY SEVEN

	LEVEL 1	LEVEL 2	LEVEL 3
BREAKFAST	Garden Eggs and Tofu with Salsa* (vegan option: Deluxe Scrambled Tofu*); fresh orange juice	Garden Eggs and Tofu with Salsa* (vegan option: Deluxe Scrambled Tofu*); fresh orange juice	Garden Eggs and Tofu with Salsa* (vegan option: Deluxe Scrambled Tofu*); High Cruciferous Juice*
LUNCH	Black Bean Mango Salad*	Black Bean Mango Salad*	Black Bean Mango Salad*
DINNER	raw vegetables; Creamy Sesame Dressing/Dip*; Shiitake Broccoli Quiche*	raw vegetables; Creamy Sesame Dressing/Dip*; Thai Vegetable Curry*; brown and wild rice	raw vegetables; Creamy Sesame Dressing/Dip*; Thai Vegetable Curry*; Herbed Barley and Lentils*

options for higher-calorie diets

LUNCH – top Black Bean Mango Salad* with pumpkin seeds

DESSERT – Bluevado Pie*

WEEK 3

DAY ONE

	LEVEL 1	LEVEL 2	LEVEL 3
BREAKFAST	whole grain cereal with soy, hemp, or almond milk and ground flaxseed; fresh berries or other fruit	Blended Mango Salad*; fresh berries or other fruit	Blended Mango Salad*; fresh berries or other fruit
LUNCH	Spinach Falafel with Tahini* whole grain pita, lettuce, and tomato; melon or other fresh fruit	Spinach Falafel with Tahini* whole grain pita, lettuce, and tomato; melon or other fresh fruit	Greek Chickpea Salad*; melon or other fresh fruit
DINNER	mixed greens; Almond Balsamic Vinaigrette*; Dr. Fuhrman's Anti-Cancer Soup*	mixed greens; Almond Balsamic Vinaigrette*; Dr. Fuhrman's Anti-Cancer Soup*	mixed greens; Blueberry Pomegranate Dressing*; Dr. Fuhrman's Anti-Cancer Soup*

options for higher-calorie diets

LUNCH – sliced avocado

DESSERT – Banana Fig "Ice Cream"*

WEEK 3

DAY TWO

	LEVEL 1	LEVEL 2	LEVEL 3
BREAKFAST	Fruit and Nut Bowl*	Fruit and Nut Bowl*	Dr. Fuhrman's Fruit, Nut, and Veggie Breakfast*
LUNCH	whole grain pita triangles; Baba Ganoush*; Dr. Fuhrman's Anti-Cancer Soup* (leftover); apple or other fresh fruit	raw Vegetables; Baba Ganoush*; Dr. Fuhrman's Anti-Cancer Soup*(leftover); apple or other fresh fruit	raw Vegetables; Baba Ganoush*; Dr. Fuhrman's Anti-Cancer Soup*(leftover); apple or other fresh fruit
DINNER	mixed greens, romaine, and assorted vegetables; Green Velvet Dressing/ Dip*; Mushroom Stroganoff* over baked potato; Peach Sorbet*	mixed greens, romaine, and assorted vegetables; Green Velvet Dressing/ Dip*; Mushroom Stroganoff* over sautéed spinach; Peach Sorbet*	mixed greens, romaine, and assorted vegetables; Green Velvet Dressing/ Dip*; Mushroom Stroganoff* over sautéed spinach; Peach Sorbet*

options for higher-calorie diets
> **LUNCH** – apple slices with raw cashew or almond butter

DAY THREE

	LEVEL 1	LEVEL 2	LEVEL 3
BREAKFAST	Antioxidant-Rich Breakfast Bars*; 100 percent fruit juice	Antioxidant-Rich Breakfast Bars*; 100 percent fruit juice	Antioxidant-Rich Breakfast Bars*; High Cruciferious Juice*
LUNCH	turkey (vegan option: Tasty Hummus*) on sprouted wheat bread with mixed greens, broccoli sprouts, tomato, and mustard; grapes or other fresh fruit	turkey (vegan option: Tasty Hummus*) on sprouted wheat bread with mixed greens, broccoli sprouts, tomato, and mustard; grapes or other fresh fruit	Carrot's Original Micro Salad*; grapes or other fresh fruit
DINNER	raw vegetables; Fast Black Bean Soup*	Creamy Cruciferous Curry*; steamed vegetables with Almond Tomato Sauce*	Creamy Cruciferous Curry*; steamed vegetables with Almond Tomato Sauce*

options for higher-calorie diets

DESSERT – Blueberry Banana Cobbler*

DAY FOUR

	LEVEL 1	LEVEL 2	LEVEL 3
BREAKFAST	Cinnamon Fruit Oatmeal*	Cinnamon Fruit Oatmeal*	Cinnamon Fruit Oatmeal*
LUNCH	mixed greens and assorted vegetables; Ten Thousand Island Dressing*; Easy Vegetable Pizza*; watermelon or other fresh fruit	mixed greens and assorted vegetables; Ten Thousand Island Dressing*; Creamy Cruciferous Curry* (leftover); watermelon or other fresh fruit	mixed greens and assorted vegetables; Ten Thousand Island Dressing*; Creamy Cruciferous Curry* (leftover); watermelon or other fresh fruit
DINNER	whole grain pita triangles; Perfect Pesto*; Mediterranean Fish Stew*; fresh strawberries	raw vegetables; Perfect Pesto*; Mediterranean Fish Stew*; fresh strawberries	raw vegetables; Perfect Pesto*; Mediterranean Fish Stew*; steamed broccoli or other fresh vegetable; fresh strawberries

options for higher-calorie diets

    DINNER – Acorn Squash Supreme*

    DESSERT – fresh strawberries with Chocolate Dip*

WEEK 3

DAY FIVE

	LEVEL 1	LEVEL 2	LEVEL 3
BREAKFAST	fruit and berries with plain or vanilla nonfat yogurt	Chocolate Cherry Smoothie*	Chocolate Cherry Smoothie*
LUNCH	mixed greens and arugula salad; choice of Dr. Fuhrman's healthful salad dressings; berries or other fresh fruit	mixed greens and arugula salad; choice of Dr. Fuhrman's healthful salad dressings; berries or other fresh fruit	Nutra-Green Salad with Black Fig Dressing*; berries or other fresh fruit
DINNER	raw vegetables; Eggplant Hummus*; Southwest Vegetable Stew*; steamed green beans	raw vegetables; Eggplant Hummus*; Quick and Creamy Vegetable Bean Soup*	raw vegetables; Eggplant Hummus*; Quick and Creamy Vegetable Bean Soup*

options for higher-calorie diets

LUNCH – add beans and/or nuts to salad

DESSERT – Yummy Banana Oat Bars*

DAY SIX

	LEVEL 1	LEVEL 2	LEVEL 3
BREAKFAST	Apple Supreme*	Apple Supreme*	Apple Supreme*
LUNCH	carrot and celery sticks; Southwest Vegetable Stew* (leftover); apple or other fresh fruit	Triple Treat Cabbage Salad*; Quick and Creamy Vegetable Bean Stew* (leftover); apple or other fresh fruit	Triple Treat Cabbage Salad*; Quick and Creamy Vegetable Bean Stew* (leftover); apple or other fresh fruit
DINNER	romaine and mixed greens salad with assorted vegetables; purchased low-fat/low-sodium dressing; Cuban Black Beans* with brown and wild rice	romaine and mixed greens salad with assorted vegetables; Zesty Avocado Dressing/Dip*; Cuban Black Beans* with brown and wild rice	romaine and mixed greens salad with assorted vegetables; Zesty Avocado Dressing/Dip*; Portobello Mushrooms and Beans*; Swiss Chard with Garlic and Lemon*

options for higher-calorie diets

DINNER – baked sweet potato

DESSERT – Frozen Banana Fluff*

DAY SEVEN

	LEVEL 1	LEVEL 2	LEVEL 3
BREAKFAST	Scrambled Veggies and Eggs* (vegan option: Deluxe Scrambled Tofu*); berries or other fresh fruit	Scrambled Veggies and Eggs* (vegan option: Deluxe Scrambled Tofu*); berries or other fresh fruit	Scrambled Veggies and Eggs* (vegan option: Deluxe Scrambled Tofu*); berries or other fresh fruit
LUNCH	Healthy Slaw*; pita stuffed with mixed greens, black beans, avocado, and choice of Dr. Fuhrman's healthful salad dressings; orange or other fresh fruit	Healthy Slaw*, pita stuffed with mixed greens, black beans, avocado, and choice of Dr. Fuhrman's healthful salad dressings; orange or other fresh fruit	Healthy Slaw*; In a Hurry Anti-Cancer Soup*; orange or other fresh fruit
DINNER	mixed greens salad with assorted vegetables; Cashew Caesar Dressing*; No-Meat Balls*; no-salt-added or low-sodium tomato sauce; whole wheat pasta	mixed greens salad with assorted vegetables; Cashew Caesar Dressing*; No-Meat Balls*; no-salt-added or low-sodium tomato sauce; baked spaghetti squash	mixed greens salad with assorted vegetables; Cashew Caesar Dressing*; No-Pasta Vegetable Lasagna*

options for higher-calorie diets
> **DESSERT** – Mixed Berry Freeze*

DAY ONE

LEVEL 1	LEVEL 2	LEVEL 3
BREAKFAST		
Tropical Mint Smoothie*	Antioxidant-Rich Smoothie*	Antioxidant-Rich Smoothie*
LUNCH		
Vegetable Garbanzo Wrap*; pear or other fresh fruit	Vegetable Garbanzo Wrap*; pear or other fresh fruit	Quick Vegetable Bean Medley* on a bed of watercress or arugula
DINNER		
raw vegetables; Island Black Bean Dip*; Shiitake Broccoli Quiche*	raw vegetables; Island Black Bean Dip*; Vegetable Shepherd's Pie*	raw vegetables; Island Black Bean Dip*; Vegetable Shepherd's Pie*

options for higher-calorie diets

BREAKFAST – Banana Cashew Lettuce Wrap*

DESSERT – Wild Apple Crunch*

DAY TWO

	LEVEL 1	LEVEL 2	LEVEL 3
BREAKFAST	Healthy Pancakes*; Fruit and Berry Compote*	old-fashioned oatmeal; Fruit and Berry Compote*	old-fashioned oatmeal; Fruit and Berry Compote*; Mixed Vegetable Juice*
LUNCH	Quinoa Bean Salad* over baby greens; cherries or other fresh fruit	Quinoa Bean Salad* over baby greens; cherries or other fresh fruit	Quinoa Bean Salad* over baby greens; cherries or other fresh fruit
DINNER	Asian Vegetable Stir-Fry* with added cooked chicken; shrimp or scallops if desired; Strawberry Pineapple Sorbet*	Asian Vegetable Stir- Fry*; Strawberry Pineapple Sorbet*	Asian Vegetable Stir- Fry*; Strawberry Pineapple Sorbet*

options for higher-calorie diets

DESSERT – top Strawberry Pineapple Sorbet* with Macadamia Cream*

WEEK 4

DAY THREE

LEVEL 1	LEVEL 2	LEVEL 3
BREAKFAST Blueberry Orange Smoothie*	Blueberry Orange Smoothie*	Super-Easy Blended Salad*
LUNCH turkey on whole grain pita with mixed greens, broccoli sprouts, and mustard (vegan option: substitute raw nut butter or avocado for turkey); grapes or other fresh fruit	mixed greens and watercress salad topped with white beans; choice of Dr. Fuhrman's healthful salad dressings*; grapes or other fresh fruit	mixed greens and watercress salad topped with white beans; choice of Dr. Fuhrman's healthful salad dressings*; grapes or other fresh fruit
DINNER Stuffed Artichokes*; Speedy Vegetable and Bean Soup*	Stuffed Artichokes*; Speedy Vegetable and Bean Soup*	Stuffed Artichokes*; Speedy Vegetable and Bean Soup*; Swiss Chard with Garlic and Lemon*

options for higher-calorie diets

BREAKFAST – unsulfured dry fruit

whole grain toast with trans-fat-free spread

DAY FOUR

	LEVEL 1	LEVEL 2	LEVEL 3
BREAKFAST	Fruit and Nut Bowl*	Fruit and Nut Bowl*	Fruit and Nut Bowl*
LUNCH	raw vegetables; Tuscan White Bean Dip*; Easy Vegetable Pizza*	raw vegetables; Tuscan White Bean Dip*; Speedy Vegetable and Bean Soup* (leftover)	raw vegetables; Tuscan White Bean Dip*; Speedy Vegetable and Bean Soup* (leftover)
DINNER	Broccoli Vinaigrette*; Bean Enchiladas*; strawberries with toasted unsweetened coconut	Broccoli Vinaigrette*; Bean Enchiladas*; strawberries with toasted unsweetened coconut	Broccoli Vinaigrette*; Mediterranean Bean and Kale Sauté*; strawberries with toasted unsweetened coconut

options for higher-calorie diets

DESSERT – Chocolate Cherry "Ice Cream"*

WEEK 4

DAY FIVE

	LEVEL 1	LEVEL 2	LEVEL 3
BREAKFAST	Special Oatmeal*	Special Oatmeal*	Special Oatmeal*
LUNCH	whole wheat pita with Baba Ganoush*, mixed greens, sun-dried tomatoes, and chopped red pepper; pineapple or other fresh fruit	whole wheat pita with Baba Ganoush*, mixed greens, sun-dried tomatoes, and chopped red pepper; pineapple or other fresh fruit	steamed vegetables with Sesame Ginger Sauce* on a bed of watercress; pineapple or other fresh fruit
DINNER	mixed greens with assorted vegetables; purchased low-fat/low-sodium dressing; Oriental Chicken and Broccoli* (vegan option: Sweet Potato and Asparagus Ragout*); brown rice	mixed greens with assorted vegetables; Green Velvet Dressing/Dip*; Oriental Chicken and Broccoli* (vegan option: Sweet Potato and Asparagus Ragout*); brown and wild rice	mixed greens with assorted vegetables; Green Velvet Dressing/Dip*; Oriental Chicken and Broccoli* (vegan option: Sweet Potato and Asparagus Ragout*); Great Greens*

options for higher-calorie diets

> **DINNER** – top salad with lightly toasted Mediterranean pine nuts
> **DESSERT** – Banana Nut Cookies*

WEEK 4

DAY SIX

LEVEL 1	LEVEL 2	LEVEL 3
BREAKFAST Garden Eggs and Tofu with Salsa* (vegan option: Pomegranate Muesli*)	Garden Eggs and Tofu with Salsa* (vegan option: Pomegranate Muesli*)	Garden Eggs and Tofu with Salsa* (vegan option: Pomegranate Muesli*)
LUNCH Spicy Bean Spread/ Dip*; whole grain pita triangles; Gazpacho Summer Soup*; orange or other fresh fruit	Spicy Bean Spread/ Dip*; endive spears; Gazpacho Summer Soup*; orange or other fresh fruit	Spicy Bean Spread/ Dip*; endive spears; Gazpacho Summer Soup*; orange or other fresh fruit
DINNER Pistachio Crusted Tempeh with Balsamic Marinade and Shiitake Mushrooms*; brown and wild rice mixed with snow peas; cherries or other fresh fruit	Pistachio Crusted Tempeh with Balsamic Marinade and Shiitake Mushrooms*; Spaghetti Squash Primavera*; cherries or other fresh fruit	Pistachio Crusted Tempeh with Balsamic Marinade and Shiitake Mushrooms*; Great Greens*; cherries or other fresh fruit

options for higher-calorie diets;

    BREAKFAST – sprouted grain bread

    DESSERT – Wild Apple Crunch*

DAY SEVEN

	LEVEL 1	LEVEL 2	LEVEL 3
BREAKFAST	Apple Pie Smoothie*	Quinoa Breakfast Pudding*	Quinoa Breakfast Pudding*; Mixed Vegetable Juice*
LUNCH	Pom Salad with Figs and Pumpkin Seeds*; pear or other fresh fruit	Pom Salad with Figs and Pumpkin Seeds*; pear or other fresh fruit	Pom Salad with Figs and Pumpkin Seeds*; pear or other fresh fruit
DINNER	Healthy Slaw*; Roasted Vegetable Pizza*	In a Hurry Anti-Cancer Soup*; Eggplant Stuffed with Tofu Purée*	In a Hurry Anti-Cancer Soup*; Eggplant Stuffed with Tofu Purée*

options for higher-calorie diets

DESSERT – Healthy Chocolate Cake*

SECTION 2

RECIPES

THREE STEPS RECIPE INDEX

Non-Vegan Dishes

Desserts

SMOOTHIES, BLENDED SALADS, AND JUICES

serves: **2**

prep time: **5 minutes**

INGREDIENTS

4 cups baby spinach

4 cups romaine lettuce

1 cup pomegranate
juice (or seeds from
one pomegranate)

1 cup frozen blueberries

1 cup frozen strawberries

4 dates, pitted

2 tablespoons
ground flaxseed

½ avocado

ANTIOXIDANT-RICH SMOOTHIE

DIRECTIONS

Blend all ingredients together in a high-powered
blender until smooth and creamy.

APPLE PIE SMOOTHIE

serves: **2**

prep time: **5 minutes**

INGREDIENTS

2 medium apples*,
cored

3 dates, pitted

¼ cup walnuts

¼ cup raisins

1 teaspoon cinnamon

¼ teaspoon vanilla

1 tablespoon
ground flaxseed

1 cup soy, hemp,
or almond milk

DIRECTIONS

Blend all ingredients in a high-powered blender
until smooth and creamy.

* *No need to peel apple if organic.*

BLENDED MANGO SALAD

serves: **2**

prep time: **5 minutes**

INGREDIENTS

2 ripe mangos

1 cup spinach, chopped

4 cups chopped romaine lettuce

¼ cup unsweetened soy, hemp, or almond milk

DIRECTIONS

Peel and chop mangos and place in food processor or high-powered blender.

Add spinach and half the lettuce. Blend until well combined. Add the milk and remaining lettuce. Blend until creamy.

BLUEBERRY ORANGE SMOOTHIE

serves: **2**

prep time: **5 minutes**

INGREDIENTS

3 dates, pitted

2 oranges, peeled and seeded

1 banana

1 cup frozen blueberries

1 tablespoon ground flaxseed

DIRECTIONS

Blend all ingredients together in a high-powered blender until smooth and creamy.

CHOCOLATE CHERRY SMOOTHIE

serves: **2**

prep time: **6 minutes**

INGREDIENTS

4 ounces organic
baby spinach

½ cup unsweetened soy,
hemp, or almond milk

½ cup pomegranate juice,
cherry juice, or cherry
pomegranate juice

1 tablespoon Dr. Fuhrman's
Cocoa Powder or other
natural cocoa powder,
not Dutch processed

1 cup frozen cherries

1 banana

1 cup frozen blueberries

½ teaspoon vanilla extract

2 tablespoons
ground flaxseed

DIRECTIONS

If using a regular blender, liquefy the spinach
with milk and juice. Add remaining ingredients
and blend about 2 minutes until very smooth. If
using a high-powered blender, blend all at once.

HONEYDEW BERRY SMOOTHIE

serves: **2**

prep time: **5 minutes**

INGREDIENTS

4 cups honeydew melon, cut into 1-inch pieces

2 cups frozen blackberries

4 pitted dates

DIRECTIONS

Blend ingredients in a high-powered blender until smooth and creamy.

TROPICAL MINT SMOOTHIE

serves: **1**

prep time: **5 minutes**

INGREDIENTS

½ cup pineapple,
fresh or frozen

1 cup fresh mango,
peeled and cut into
chunks, or frozen mango

2 medium oranges,
peeled and seeded

1 cup baby spinach

6 large mint leaves

DIRECTIONS

Blend all ingredients in a high-powered blender
until smooth and creamy.

RASPBERRY FROSTY BLENDED SALAD

serves: **2**

prep time: **5 minutes**

INGREDIENTS

1 cup frozen
organic spinach

1 cup frozen raspberries

8 cups (about 8 ounces)
romaine lettuce

3 whole oranges,
peeled and seeded

DIRECTIONS

Blend all ingredients in a high-powered blender.

serves: **1**

prep time: **5 minutes**

INGREDIENTS

8 ounces baby greens

1 orange, peeled
and seeded

juice of ¼ lemon

SUPER-EASY BLENDED SALAD

DIRECTIONS

Blend ingredients in a high-powered blender until smooth and creamy.

HIGH CRUCIFEROUS JUICE

serves: **4**

prep time: **20 minutes**

INGREDIENTS

6 medium carrots

6 cauliflower florets

2 apples, quartered

1 bunch kale

½ bunch watercress

½ head broccoli
with stems

DIRECTIONS

Run all ingredients through a juicer.

MIXED VEGETABLE JUICE

serves: **3**

prep time: **20 minutes**

INGREDIENTS

6 kale leaves

8 carrots, peeled

2 stalks bok choy

2 apples

2 medium beets, peeled

1 cup watercress with stems

DIRECTIONS

Run all ingredients through a juicer.

SUNRISE JUICE

serves: **2**
prep time: **5 minutes**

INGREDIENTS

2 cups fresh pineapple

1 cup baby carrots

⅛ slice lemon,
without rind

1 tablespoon Goji berries

1 cup ice cubes

DIRECTIONS

Blend all ingredients together in a high-powered blender.

BREAKFASTS

ANTIOXIDANT-RICH BREAKFAST BARS

serves: **5**

prep time: **15 minutes**

INGREDIENTS

1 medium ripe banana

1 cup old-fashioned rolled oats

1 cup frozen blueberries, thawed

¼ cup raisins

⅛ cup pomegranate juice

2 tablespoons finely chopped dates

1 tablespoon chopped walnuts

1 tablespoon Goji berries

1 tablespoon raw sunflower seeds

2 tablespoons ground flaxseed

DIRECTIONS

Preheat oven to 350°F.

Mash banana in a large bowl. Add remaining ingredients and mix thoroughly.

Lightly wipe an 8"x8" baking pan with a small amount of olive oil. Spread mixture into pan. Bake for 25 minutes. Cool on wire rack and cut into bars.

Refrigerate any leftover bars.

APPLE SUPREME

serves: **4**
prep time: **20 minutes**

INGREDIENTS

6 apples, cored, peeled, and chopped

1 teaspoon cinnamon

½ cup chopped walnuts

3 pitted dates

1 tablespoon ground flaxseed

¼ cup unsweetened soy, almond, or hemp milk

½ cup raisins

½ cup old-fashioned rolled oats

DIRECTIONS

Preheat oven to 350°F.

In a high-powered blender, combine one cup of the chopped apples with cinnamon, walnuts, dates, flaxseed, and soy milk. Pour over remaining chopped apples. Add raisins and mix well. Sprinkle oats on top. Bake for 15 minutes.

BANANA CASHEW LETTUCE WRAP

serves: **2**

prep time: **5 minutes**

INGREDIENTS

¼ cup raw
cashew butter

12 romaine
lettuce leaves

2 bananas,
thinly sliced

DIRECTIONS

Spread about 1 teaspoon cashew butter on each lettuce leaf. Lay a few banana slices on the butter and roll up like a burrito.

CINNAMON FRUIT OATMEAL

serves: **2**

prep time: **15 minutes**

INGREDIENTS

1 cup water

1 teaspoon vanilla extract

¼ teaspoon cinnamon

½ cup old-fashioned rolled oats

½ cup blueberries

2 apples, chopped

2 tablespoons chopped walnuts

1 tablespoon ground flaxseed

¼ cup raisins

DIRECTIONS

In a saucepan, combine water with the vanilla and cinnamon. Bring to a boil over high heat. Reduce heat to a simmer and stir in the oats.

When the mixture starts to simmer, add the blueberries. Remove from heat when berries are heated through.

Cover and let stand for 15 minutes until thick and creamy.

Mix in apples, nuts, flaxseed, and raisins.

DR. FUHRMAN'S FRUIT, NUT, AND VEGGIE BREAKFAST

serves: **2**

prep time: **20 minutes**

INGREDIENTS

¼ cup diced fennel bulb

1 medium cucumber,
peeled, cut lengthwise,
thinly sliced

1 cup fresh or frozen
blueberries, thawed

1 cup organic
strawberries, sliced

½ green apple,
peeled and sliced

⅓ cup chopped walnuts

SAUCE

½ cup raw cashews or
⅓ cup raw cashew butter

½ cup soy, hemp,
or almond milk

3 pitted dates

DIRECTIONS

Combine vegetables, fruits, and nuts.

Combine sauce ingredients in a high-powered blender until smooth.

Pour sauce over vegetable/fruit bowl and mix thoroughly.

FRUIT AND BERRY COMPOTE

serves: **4**

prep time: **10 minutes**

INGREDIENTS

2 cups cubed fresh pineapple

1 cup halved organic strawberries

1 cup frozen cherries (pitted), thawed

1 cup dried fruit of choice, chopped (optional)

¼ cup orange juice

2 oranges, peeled and cut into bite-sized pieces

1 pear, peeled and cubed

½ cup unsweetened shredded coconut

DIRECTIONS

Combine all ingredients with half the coconut, and leave the remaining coconut to sprinkle on top. Chill for 2 hours or refrigerate overnight.

FRUIT AND NUT BOWL

serves: **2**
prep time: **10 minutes**

INGREDIENTS

1 apple, cut into slices

1 banana, sliced

1 orange, sectioned

½ cup blueberries

½ cup sliced organic strawberries

2 tablespoons sliced raw almonds

2 tablespoons raw chopped walnuts

DIRECTIONS

Combine fruit and berries. Add nuts and toss gently.

HEALTHY PANCAKES (NON-VEGAN)

serves: **2**

prep time: **10 minutes**

INGREDIENTS

1 cup cooked great northern beans or canned, no-salt-added or low-sodium, drained

2 egg whites

1 cup soy, hemp, or almond milk

1 teaspoon vanilla

5 pitted dates

½ cup oat bran

¼ cup buckwheat flour

1 cup blueberries or 1 banana, sliced

DIRECTIONS

Blend beans, egg whites, soy milk, vanilla, and dates in a high-powered blender until smooth. Add oat bran and buckwheat flour and blend.

Fold in blueberries or banana.

Pour batter by ¼ cupfuls onto a hot, nonstick or lightly oiled griddle. When bubbles form on top of pancakes, flip. Cook until golden.

POMEGRANATE MUESLI

serves: **2**
prep time: **10 minutes**

INGREDIENTS

½ cup pomegranate juice

¼ cup steel-cut or
old-fashioned rolled oats
(not quick or instant)

1 apple, peeled
and grated

4 raw cashews or
hazelnuts, coarsely
chopped

½ cup halved grapes

½ cup cubed cantaloupe

½ cup sliced fresh
organic strawberries

1 tablespoon currants

1 tablespoon
ground flaxseed

DIRECTIONS

Soak oats in pomegranate juice overnight in refrigerator. Oats will absorb the liquid. In the morning, combine oats with remaining ingredients.

YOU MAY ADD OR
SUBSTITUTE ANY
FRUITS ACCORDING
TO TASTE

QUICK BANANA BERRY BREAKFAST TO GO

serves: **2**

prep time: **8 minutes**

INGREDIENTS

2 cups fresh or frozen blueberries

2 bananas, sliced

½ cup old-fashioned rolled oats

⅓ cup pomegranate juice

2 tablespoons chopped walnuts

1 tablespoon raw sunflower seeds

2 tablespoons dried currants

DIRECTIONS

Combine all ingredients in a small microwave-proof bowl. Heat in the microwave for 3 minutes.

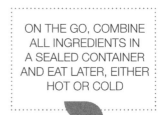

ON THE GO, COMBINE ALL INGREDIENTS IN A SEALED CONTAINER AND EAT LATER, EITHER HOT OR COLD

QUINOA
BREAKFAST PUDDING

serves: **8**

prep time: **20 minutes**

INGREDIENTS

¾ cup quinoa

3 cups water

12 dates, pitted

2 cups unsweetened soy, hemp, or almond milk

1 teaspoon vanilla

⅛ cup slivered raw almonds

⅛ cup coarsely ground walnuts

½ cup dried currants

1 cup finely chopped organic baby spinach

1 cup finely chopped kale leaves

⅛ teaspoon cinnamon

DIRECTIONS

Preheat oven to 350°F.

Wash quinoa in a bowl, then drain through a fine screen strainer. In a large saucepan, bring quinoa and water to a boil. Reduce heat and simmer, uncovered, until grains are translucent and the mixture is the consistency of a thick porridge, about 15 minutes.

Blend dates, soy milk, and vanilla. Combine with quinoa, nuts, currants, spinach, and kale. Pour into a lightly oiled baking pan, sprinkle with cinnamon, and bake for 30 minutes.

May be served warm or cold.

SPECIAL OATMEAL

serves: **4**
prep time: **20 minutes**

INGREDIENTS

1¾ cups water

1 cup old-fashioned
rolled oats

4 pitted dates, chopped

¼ teaspoon coriander

2 bananas, sliced

1 cup chopped or
grated apple

1 cup fresh or
frozen blueberries

2 tablespoons
ground flaxseed

DIRECTIONS

In a saucepan, bring the water to a boil and stir
in all ingredients except blueberries and ground
flaxseed. Simmer for 5 minutes.

Stir in blueberries. Sprinkle flaxseed on top or stir
in. Cover for 2-3 minutes before serving.

If desired, this recipe may be made in the oven.

Preheat oven to 350°F.

In a baking dish, combine all ingredients,
except for the bananas, apples, blueberries,
and flaxseed. Bake uncovered for 30 minutes.
Add the bananas and more water, if desired.
Bake another 15 minutes. Stir in apple and
blueberries. Sprinkle flaxseed on top.

TROPICAL FRUIT SALAD

serves: **4**

prep time: **20 minutes**

INGREDIENTS

2 cups cubed pineapple

1 cup cubed mango

1 cup cubed papaya

2 oranges, peeled
and sliced

1 banana, sliced

2 tablespoons
unsweetened
shredded coconut

shredded romaine lettuce

DIRECTIONS

Toss fruit together. Add coconut and serve on top of lettuce.

WILD BLUEBERRY HOT BREAKFAST

serves: **1**

prep time: **5 minutes**

INGREDIENTS

2 cups frozen wild blueberries

½ cup soy, hemp, or almond milk

¼ cup unsweetened shredded coconut, lightly toasted

¼ cup chopped walnuts

¼ cup currants

1 banana, sliced

DIRECTIONS

Heat frozen blueberries and soy milk until warm. Add remaining ingredients and stir well.

SALADS

ARUGULA SALAD WITH SUN-DRIED TOMATO DRESSING

serves: **4**

prep time: **15 minutes**

INGREDIENTS

-SALAD-

12 ounces arugula

1 tablespoon fresh chopped rosemary

1 tablespoon fresh chopped basil

1 tablespoon fresh chopped thyme

1 cup grape tomatoes

½ cup chopped red onion

-DRESSING-

1 cup sun-dried tomatoes

1 ripe tomato

½ cup unsweetened soy, almond, or hemp milk

1 lemon, juiced

1 raw garlic clove

DIRECTIONS

Soak the sun-dried tomatoes in the soy milk for an hour. Then combine all dressing ingredients in a high-powered blender until smooth. Pour over salad.

ASPARAGUS SHIITAKE SALAD WITH CREAMY SESAME DRESSING

INGREDIENTS

-CREAMY SESAME DRESSING-

⅔ cup plus 2 tablespoons unhulled sesame seeds, divided

1 cup unsweetened soy, hemp, or almond milk

2 tablespoons Dr. Fuhrman's Riesling Raisin Vinegar or seasoned rice vinegar

1 tablespoon raw cashew butter or 2 tablespoons raw cashews

1 teaspoon toasted sesame oil

7 dates, pitted and soaked in water 30 minutes
(reserve the water)

1 clove raw garlic

-SALAD-

2 medium beets, peeled and sliced into ½-inch pieces

½ cup water

8 ounces shiitake mushrooms, sliced

1 pound fresh asparagus, cut diagonally into 2-inch slices

1 tablespoon Dr. Fuhrman's VegiZest or other no-salt soup base seasoning

1 teaspoon garlic powder

1 medium red bell pepper, seeded and thinly sliced

½ cup sliced water chestnuts

4 cups watercress

2 cups bean sprouts

DIRECTIONS

Lightly toast 2 tablespoons of sesame seeds in a pan over medium heat for 3 minutes, shaking the pan frequently. Set aside.

In a food processor or high-powered blender, blend remaining ⅔ cup sesame seeds along with the other dressing ingredients, until smooth and creamy. Stir in toasted sesame seeds. Use soaking water from dates to thin if needed.

To make the salad, preheat the oven to 400°F. Place beets and water in a baking pan. Cover and roast for 20 minutes. Uncover and continue roasting until tender. If needed, add more water to keep beets from drying out. Set aside.

Meanwhile, water sauté mushrooms over high heat for about 4 minutes, using only enough water to keep from scorching. When mushrooms are tender and juicy, add the asparagus and water sauté until slightly tender but still crisp, about 5 minutes. Toss with VegiZest and garlic powder. Remove from heat and toss with bell pepper and water chestnuts.

Place watercress on a plate and pile the vegetable mixture on top. Drizzle dressing over all, topping with the bean sprouts. Arrange roasted beets around the sides.

BLACK BEAN MANGO SALAD

serves: **6**
prep time: **20 minutes**

INGREDIENTS

1 mango, peeled, pitted, and cubed

2 tablespoons chopped fresh cilantro

4 green onions, thinly sliced

1 medium red bell pepper, seeded and chopped

1 cup frozen corn, thawed, or 2-3 ears fresh corn, husked, silks removed

3 cups cooked black beans, or 2 (15-ounce) cans, no-salt-added or low-sodium, drained and rinsed

3 tablespoons fresh lime juice

1 teaspoon minced fresh garlic

1 teaspoon dried oregano

1 teaspoon ground cumin

dash chili powder

9 cups finely chopped romaine lettuce

DIRECTIONS

If using fresh corn on the cob, steam or boil for 3-5 minutes or until tender. Drain and cool. Cut kernels off the cob, cutting close to the cob.

Mix all the ingredients, except the lettuce. Allow salad to stand at least 15 minutes before serving. Serve on a bed of chopped green lettuce.

The vegetable mixture can be made a day ahead and refrigerated. To do so, combine all the ingredients except the mango. Add the mango and a splash of lime juice just before serving.

CARROT'S ORIGINAL MICRO SALAD

serves: **1**

prep time: **10 minutes**

INGREDIENTS

2 medium carrots, peeled

¼ small head cabbage

1 cup broccoli pieces

2 medium stalks celery

1 large apple, cored

¼ cup pecans
or other raw nuts

1 teaspoon
ground flaxseed

DIRECTIONS

Using the S blade of a food processor, process ingredients until finely chopped, approximately the size of confetti. Pulse (turn on and off) several times during chopping.

These ingredients store well, so recipe can be increased to provide several servings.

GREEK CHICKPEA SALAD

serves: **4**

prep time: **25 minutes**

INGREDIENTS

1½ cups cooked garbanzo beans (chickpeas) or canned, no-salt-added or low-sodium, drained

3 plum tomatoes, chopped

1 boiled potato, peeled and chopped in chunks

1 green apple, peeled, cored, and chopped

1 cucumber, chopped

½ small onion, chopped

¼ cup chopped Brazil nuts, divided

3 tablespoons Dr. Fuhrman's Spicy Pecan Vinegar

1 teaspoon chopped cilantro

10 ounces mixed salad greens

DIRECTIONS

Mix all ingredients except for the salad greens and 2 tablespoons of the Brazil nuts. Serve on bed of mixed salad greens. Sprinkle with the 2 tablespoons of Brazil nuts.

THIS IS EVEN BETTER WHEN REFRIGERATED OVERNIGHT TO BLEND FLAVORS

HEALTHY SLAW

serves: **3**
prep time: **20 minutes**

INGREDIENTS

-SLAW-

2 cups shredded apples

1 cup shredded
raw cabbage

1 cup shredded raw beets

1 cup shredded
raw carrots

½ cup raisins

-DRESSING-

½ cup soft tofu

¼ cup soy, almond,
or hemp milk

1 tablespoon Dr. Fuhrman's
Riesling Raisin Vinegar

1 tablespoon Dr. Fuhrman's
Spicy Pecan Vinegar

1 tablespoon date sugar,
or 3 pitted dates

2 teaspoons fresh
lemon juice

¼ cup chopped pecans,
lightly toasted*

DIRECTIONS

Combine slaw ingredients.

Blend dressing ingredients and toss with slaw.
Top with toasted pecans.

* *Lightly toast pecans in a 200°F oven for 3
minutes.*

NUTRA-GREEN SALAD WITH BLACK FIG DRESSING

serves: **4**

prep time: **20 minutes**

INGREDIENTS

3 ounces mache*

3 ounces watercress

2 ounces frisée

4 ounces mixed
baby greens

1 cup broccoli sprouts

⅓ cup Dr. Fuhrman's
Black Fig Vinegar

1 teaspoon Dr. Fuhrman's
VegiZest

4 tablespoons water

1 tablespoon
Dijon mustard

1 teaspoon dried
marjoram

1 tablespoon raw
almond butter

1 tablespoon ketchup,
low-sodium

1 teaspoon garlic powder

½ cup pecans,
coarsely chopped

DIRECTIONS

Wash and dry the first 5 ingredients and
place in a large salad bowl. Whisk remaining
ingredients, except for the pecans, until smooth.
Toss salad with dressing, and serve on plates
topped with chopped pecans.

* Mache is a mild salad lettuce with round small
leaves. Use additional baby greens if mache
is not available.

POM SALAD WITH FIGS AND PUMPKIN SEEDS

serves: **2**

prep time: **20 minutes**

INGREDIENTS

-DRESSING-

½ cup pomegranate juice, or the seeds from 1 pomegranate

⅓ cup Dr. Fuhrman's Black Fig Vinegar or balsamic vinegar

2 dates, pitted

1 tablespoon chopped shallots

1 clove garlic

½ cup raw pumpkin seeds

-SALAD-

5 cups romaine lettuce

2 cups arugula

1 cup radicchio

1 cup dried unsulfured figs, soaked overnight, then sliced

¼ cup raw pumpkin seeds, lightly toasted*

½ cup pomegranate kernels, optional (if in season)

DIRECTIONS

Blend dressing ingredients in a food processor or high-powered blender. Toss lettuce, arugula, and radicchio with figs and dressing. Sprinkle with pumpkin seeds and, if available, pomegranate kernels.

* *Toast pumpkin seeds in a skillet over medium high heat, stirring frequently, until seeds are puffed and beginning to brown, 2-3 minutes. Transfer to a large plate to cool.*

QUINOA BEAN SALAD

serves: **6**

prep time: **25 minutes**

INGREDIENTS

2 cups cooked quinoa

1½ cups cooked white beans, or 1 (15-ounce) can, no-salt-added or low-sodium, drained

1 cup grated carrots

1 cup currants

½ cup raw walnuts, chopped

2 plum tomatoes, chopped

1 small red onion, thinly sliced

½ green bell pepper, chopped

½ red bell pepper, chopped

½ orange or yellow bell pepper, chopped

3 cloves garlic, minced

1 tablespoon chili powder

2 teaspoons Bragg Liquid Aminos or low-sodium soy sauce

DIRECTIONS

Cook quinoa according to package directions. Place all other ingredients in a large bowl and mix. Add cooked quinoa and toss.

THIS IS EVEN BETTER WHEN REFRIGERATED OVERNIGHT TO BLEND FLAVORS

SOUTHERN-STYLE MIXED SALAD

serves: **2**

prep time: **15 minutes**

INGREDIENTS

1 cup water

2 cloves garlic, minced

dash black pepper

1½ cup cooked black-eyed peas, or
1 (15-ounce) can, no-salt added or low-sodium, drained and rinsed

1 cup seeded and chopped yellow bell pepper

1 cup chopped
fresh tomato

⅓ cup chopped
fresh parsley

½ cup chopped
red onion

2 tablespoons
Dr. Fuhrman's Black
Fig Vinegar or
balsamic vinegar

10 ounces (about 7 cups)
mixed salad greens

DIRECTIONS

Combine the water, garlic, and black pepper in a large saucepan; bring to a boil. Add black-eyed peas; cover and simmer over low heat for 10 minutes. Drain. In a bowl, combine the black-eyed peas, bell pepper, tomato, parsley, onion, and vinegar. Cover and chill for 3 hours or overnight. Serve over the salad greens.

* *If you can't find no-salt-added or low-sodium black-eyed peas, use no-salt-added or low-sodium small white beans instead.*

SPINACH AND GARBANZO BEAN SALAD WITH LEMON FIG DRESSING

INGREDIENTS

-SALAD-

1 cup mushrooms, thinly sliced

12 ounces organic baby spinach

1½ cups cooked garbanzo beans (chickpeas), or 1 (15-ounce) can, no-salt-added or low-sodium, drained

1 cup shredded carrots

1 cup broccoli florets

1 cup chopped tomatoes

-DRESSING-

¼ cup fresh lemon juice

2 cloves garlic, minced

½ teaspoon dried parsley

½ teaspoon dried basil

¼ teaspoon onion powder

¼ teaspoon ground mustard seed

¼ cup Dr. Fuhrman's Black Fig Vinegar

DIRECTIONS

Water sauté mushrooms for 3 minutes and add to salad ingredients. Whisk all dressing ingredients together. Pour over salad.

TRIPLE TREAT CABBAGE SALAD

serves: **4**

prep time: **15 minutes**

INGREDIENTS

-SALAD-

2 cups green cabbage, grated

1 cup red cabbage, grated

1 cup savoy cabbage, grated

1 carrot, peeled and grated

1 red pepper, sliced thin

4 tablespoons currants

2 tablespoons raw pumpkin seeds

2 tablespoons raw sunflower seeds

1 tablespoon unhulled sesame seeds

-DRESSING-

⅓ cup soy, almond, or hemp milk

1 apple, peeled and sliced

½ cup raw cashews or ¼ cup raw cashew butter

1 tablespoon Dr. Fuhrman's Spicy Pecan Vinegar

1 tablespoon currants

1 tablespoon unhulled sesame seeds, lightly toasted*

DIRECTIONS

Mix all salad ingredients together. In a high-powered blender, blend soy milk, apple, cashews, and vinegar. Toss with salad. Garnish salad with currants and lightly toasted sesame seeds.

* Lightly toast sesame seeds in a pan over medium heat for 4 minutes, shaking the pan frequently.

THIS IS GOOD MADE
A DAY AHEAD TO
ALLOW FLAVORS
TO MINGLE

WALDORF-ISH SALAD

serves: **2**

prep time: **10 minutes**

INGREDIENTS

8 ounces (about 5 cups) mixed baby greens

2 ounces (about 2 cups) arugula or watercress

3 ripe pears

¼ cup dried currants

½ cup walnuts, divided

3 tablespoons Dr. Fuhrman's D'Anjou Pear Vinegar or rice vinegar

DIRECTIONS

Crush ¼ cup of walnuts with the back of a wooden spoon. Peel and grate one of the pears. Combine the baby greens, arugula, grated pear, currants, vinegar, and crushed walnuts in a bowl. Top with the remaining pears (peeled and sliced) and walnut halves.

DRESSINGS,
DIPS,
AND SAUCES

ALMOND BALSAMIC VINAIGRETTE

serves: **5**

prep time: **8 minutes**

INGREDIENTS

½ cup water

⅓ cup roasted garlic rice vinegar

¼ cup almonds

¼ cup balsamic vinegar

¼ cup raisins

4 cloves garlic, pressed

1 teaspoon dried oregano

½ teaspoon dried basil

½ teaspoon onion powder

DIRECTIONS

Blend all ingredients together in a food processor or high-powered blender.

serves: **4**

prep time: **3 minutes**

INGREDIENTS

2 cups fresh or frozen and thawed blueberries

½ cup pomegranate juice

¼ cup raw cashews

¼ cup raw sunflower seeds

4 tablespoons Dr. Fuhrman's Blueberry Vinegar

BLUEBERRY POMEGRANATE DRESSING

DIRECTIONS

Blend all ingredients in a high-powered blender until smooth and creamy.

CASHEW CAESAR DRESSING

serves: **4**

prep time: **10 minutes**

INGREDIENTS

4 cloves garlic, roasted

½ cup unsweetened soy, almond, or hemp milk

⅓ cup raw cashew butter or ⅔ cup raw cashews

2 tablespoons nutritional yeast

1 tablespoon fresh lemon juice

1 tablespoon Dijon mustard

black pepper, to taste

DIRECTIONS

Preheat the oven to 350°F.

Break the garlic cloves apart, leaving on the papery skins. Roast for about 25 minutes or until soft.

When cool, remove the skins and blend with the remaining ingredients in a food processor or high-powered blender until creamy and smooth.

May be used for a vegetable dip or poured over 2 chopped heads (12 cups) of romaine for a Caesar Salad for two.

serves: **6**

prep time: **3 minutes**

INGREDIENTS

⅔ cup unhulled sesame
seeds, lightly toasted*

1 tablespoon raw almond
butter or 12 raw almonds

7 pitted dates

1 clove garlic

1 cup unsweetened soy,
hemp, or almond milk

2 tablespoons
Dr. Fuhrman's Riesling
Raisin Vinegar

CREAMY SESAME DRESSING/DIP

DIRECTIONS

Blend all ingredients in high-powered blender
until smooth and creamy.

* Lightly toast sesame seeds in a pan over
  medium heat for 3 minutes, shaking pan
  frequently.

serves: **4**

prep time: **10 minutes**

INGREDIENTS

1 cup water

1 cup raw pistachio nuts

4 tablespoons lemon juice

2 tablespoons
ground flaxseed

4 teaspoons
Dr. Fuhrman's VegiZest

2 teaspoons Dijon mustard

½ teaspoon garlic powder

1 teaspoon
nutritional yeast

3 dates, pitted

DIJON PISTACHIO DRESSING/DIP

DIRECTIONS

Blend all ingredients in a high-powered blender or food processor until smooth and creamy.

GREEN VELVET DRESSING/DIP

serves: **4**

prep time: **10 minutes**

INGREDIENTS

¾ cup water

½ cup fresh lemon juice

½ cup raw tahini
or sesame seeds

¼ cup chopped
fresh parsley

¼ cup chopped
fresh dill

¼ cup raw cashews or
2 tablespoons raw
cashew butter

2 tablespoons
Dr. Fuhrman's VegiZest

½ tablespoon chopped
fresh tarragon

2 cloves garlic, chopped

DIRECTIONS

Blend all ingredients in a high-powered blender until smooth.

ORANGE PEANUT DRESSING/DIP

serves: **4**

prep time: **10 minutes**

INGREDIENTS

2 oranges, peeled and seeded

¼ cup rice vinegar

⅛ cup peanut butter, no-salt-added

⅛ cup raw cashew butter or almond butter

1 teaspoon Bragg Liquid Aminos or low-sodium soy sauce

¼-inch piece fresh ginger, peeled

¼ clove garlic

DIRECTIONS

Blend all ingredients in a high-powered blender until smooth.

RUSSIAN FIG DRESSING/DIP

serves: **2**
prep time: **5 minutes**

INGREDIENTS

5 tablespoons pasta
sauce, no-salt-added
or low-sodium

3 tablespoons raw
almond butter or
¼ cup almonds

2 tablespoons raw
sunflower seeds

3 tablespoons
Dr. Fuhrman's Black
Fig Vinegar

DIRECTIONS

Blend all ingredients in a food processor or high-
powered blender until smooth.

TEN THOUSAND ISLAND DRESSING

serves: **4**

prep time: **10 minutes**

INGREDIENTS

½ cup raw cashew butter or 1 cup raw cashews

½ cup unsweetened soy, almond, or hemp milk

2 tablespoons balsamic vinegar

2 tablespoons lemon juice

1 teaspoon dried dill weed

1 teaspoon onion powder

½ teaspoon garlic powder

3 tablespoons tomato paste

2 dates, pitted

1 cucumber

¼ cup finely chopped onion

DIRECTIONS

In food processor or high-powered blender, blend the cashews, milk, vinegar, lemon juice, dill, onion powder, garlic powder, tomato paste, dates, and peeled cucumber until smooth.

Transfer to a small bowl and fold in the finely chopped onion.

TOMATO GARLIC DRESSING

serves: **2**
prep time: **5 minutes**

INGREDIENTS

½ cup low-sodium tomato or tomato-vegetable juice

2 teaspoons fresh lemon juice

½ teaspoon dried Italian seasoning

1 garlic clove, chopped

3 ounces tofu

DIRECTIONS

Blend all ingredients together in a food processor or high-powered blender.

ZESTY AVOCADO DRESSING/DIP

serves: **4**

prep time: **10 minutes**

INGREDIENTS

1 large tomato, chopped

1 avocado

⅓ cup red onion, chopped

½ cup green pepper, chopped

2 cloves garlic

2 tablespoons fresh lemon juice

2 tablespoons Dr. Fuhrman's Riesling Raisin Vinegar or balsamic vinegar

1 tablespoon Dr. Fuhrman's VegiZest or other no-salt seasoning blend

DIRECTIONS

Blend all ingredients in a high-powered blender or food processor until smooth. Add water if needed to achieve desired consistency.

BABA GANOUSH

serves: **4**

prep time: **1 hour**

INGREDIENTS

1 (1½ pound) eggplant

2 cloves garlic, chopped

2 tablespoons fresh lemon juice

1 tablespoon tahini or unhulled sesame seeds

1 tablespoon chopped flat-leaf parsley

DIRECTIONS

Preheat oven to 435°F.

Prick eggplant with a fork and place on a cookie sheet lined with foil. Bake for 50 minutes, turning occasionally, or until soft.

Let cool to touch. Peel and put all ingredients in the food processor and purée until smooth. Chill and serve with your favorite vegetables or use as a sauce in your veggie wrap or pita.

BLACK BEAN AND CORN SALSA

serves: **8**

prep time: **20 minutes**

INGREDIENTS

1½ cups cooked black beans, or 1 (15-ounce) can, no-salt-added or low-sodium, drained

1½ cups frozen white corn, thawed

4 medium fresh tomatoes, chopped

½ medium green bell pepper, chopped

1 small onion, chopped

3 large garlic cloves, chopped

2 jalapeno peppers, seeded and chopped (add more if you like a hotter salsa)

⅓ cup cilantro, finely chopped

1½ tablespoons fresh lime juice

1½ tablespoons fresh lemon juice

1 tablespoon Dr. Fuhrman's VegiZest

1 teaspoon garlic powder, or to taste

1 teaspoon Bragg Liquid Aminos

DIRECTIONS

Combine beans and corn in a mixing bowl. Place fresh tomatoes, pepper, onion, garlic, and jalapenos in a food processor and pulse until chopped into small pieces. Add to bean and corn mixture along with remaining ingredients and mix thoroughly. Serve with raw vegetables or low-salt tortilla chips.

To make your own tortilla chips, cut sprouted grain tortillas (such as Ezekiel's) into chip-sized triangles, place on baking sheet and bake at 200°F for 1 hour or until crispy, but not too well browned.

EGGPLANT HUMMUS

serves: **4**

prep time: **10 minutes**

INGREDIENTS

1 medium eggplant

1 cup cooked or
canned garbanzo beans
(chickpeas), no-salt-added
or low-sodium, drained

⅓ cup water

5 tablespoons raw
unhulled sesame seeds

2 tablespoons fresh
lemon juice

1 tablespoon dried
minced onions

4 cloves garlic,
finely chopped

dash paprika and/or
dried parsley for garnish

DIRECTIONS

Bake eggplant at 350°F for 45 minutes. Let
cool, remove skin and discard.

Blend all ingredients, including baked, peeled
eggplant, in a food processor or high-powered
blender until smooth and creamy.
Serve with assorted raw vegetables.

ISLAND BLACK BEAN DIP

serves: **6**

prep time: **10 minutes**

INGREDIENTS

1½ cups cooked black beans, or 1 (15-ounce) can, no-salt-added or low-sodium, drained and rinsed

2 teaspoons no-salt-added salsa

¼ cup scallions, minced

1½ tablespoons Dr. Fuhrman's Blood Orange Vinegar or other fruity vinegar

2 tablespoons Dr. Fuhrman's MatoZest

2 tablespoons minced red onion

½ cup finely diced mango

¼ cup diced red pepper

1 tablespoon fresh, minced cilantro, for garnish

DIRECTIONS

Remove ¼ cup of the black beans and set aside.

Place remaining beans in a blender or food processor. Add salsa, scallions, vinegar, and MatoZest. Purée until relatively smooth. Adjust seasonings to taste. Transfer to a bowl and add the reserved black beans, red onion, mango, and red bell pepper. Mix well and chill for 1 hour. Garnish with cilantro. Serve with raw vegetables.

Makes 2½ cups.

PERFECT PESTO

serves: **6**

prep time: **15 minutes**

INGREDIENTS

⅔ cup raw almonds

⅔ cup pine nuts

1 cup fresh basil leaves, packed

⅔ cup fresh parsley or cilantro leaves, packed

3 garlic cloves

1 teaspoon nutritional yeast

2 tablespoons lemon juice

1 cup chopped tomato

DIRECTIONS

In a blender or food processor, pulse to finely grind almonds and pine nuts (do not purée). Remove and place in a mixing bowl. Blend remaining ingredients in blender or food processor. Combine with nut mixture.

Use as a dip for freshly cut vegetables, or as a topping for cooked vegetables or potatoes.

SIMPLE GUACAMOLE

serves: **4**

prep time: **10 minutes**

INGREDIENTS

2 ripe avocados, peeled and pitted

½ cup finely chopped onion

¼ cup minced fresh cilantro

2 tablespoons fresh lime juice

¼ teaspoon ground cumin

¼ teaspoon freshly ground black pepper

DIRECTIONS

Using a fork, mash the avocados in a small bowl. Add the remaining ingredients and stir well. Cover and chill.

SPICY BEAN SPREAD/DIP

serves: **4**

prep time: **10 minutes**

INGREDIENTS

1⅔ cups cooked pinto beans, or 1 (15-ounce) can, no-salt-added or low-sodium, drained

¼ cup hemp seeds

1 teaspoon Dr. Fuhrman's Black Fig Vinegar or balsamic vinegar

¼ cup water

½ teaspoon crushed red chili pepper

½ teaspoon garlic powder, or two garlic cloves, crushed

1 pinch turmeric

DIRECTIONS

In a blender or food processor, purée the beans, seeds, and other ingredients. Serve with raw or lightly steamed vegetables or toasted pita bread with shredded raw greens.

TASTY HUMMUS

serves: **4**

prep time: **10 minutes**

INGREDIENTS

1 cup cooked garbanzo beans (chickpeas) or canned, no-salt-added or low-sodium, drained

¼ cup water

¼ cup raw unhulled sesame seeds

1 tablespoon lemon juice

1 tablespoon Dr. Fuhrman's VegiZest or other no-salt seasoning

1 teaspoon grated horseradish

2 small cloves garlic, chopped

2 scallions, chopped

¼ teaspoon ground cumin

DIRECTIONS

Blend all ingredients in a food processor or high-powered blender until creamy smooth. Serve with raw or lightly steamed vegetables or as a sandwich filling.

TUSCAN WHITE BEAN DIP

serves: **5**
prep time: **10 minutes**

INGREDIENTS

1½ cups cooked great
northern beans, or
1 (15-ounce) can,
no-salt-added or
low-sodium, drained

¼ cup pine nuts

2 cloves garlic, minced

1½ tablespoons
Dr. Fuhrman's MatoZest
or other no-salt seasoning
blend, to taste

1 tablespoon Dr. Fuhrman's
Black Fig Vinegar or
balsamic vinegar

1 tablespoon fresh,
minced rosemary

2 tablespoons pine nuts

¼ cup sun-dried tomatoes,
soaked in lukewarm water
until soft (about 1-2 hours),
then drained and minced

DIRECTIONS

Place all ingredients, except the sun-dried
tomatoes, in a high-powered blender or a food
processor. Process until smooth and creamy.
Adjust seasonings to taste. Stir in the minced sun-
dried tomatoes.

Chill for 1 hour before serving. Serve topped
with an extra drizzle of Dr. Fuhrman's Black Fig
Vinegar and a sprinkle of pine nuts. Enjoy with
raw vegetables.

Makes 2½ cups.

ALMOND TOMATO SAUCE

serves: **4**

prep time: **10 minutes**

INGREDIENTS

½ cup raw almonds

2 medium tomatoes

1 large garlic clove

¼ teaspoon sweet paprika

1 tablespoon red
wine vinegar

¼ cup unsweetened soy,
hemp, or almond milk

2 tablespoons chopped
fresh basil

DIRECTIONS

Process almonds and tomatoes in food processor
or high-powered blender until finely ground. Add
remaining ingredients and continue to process
until smooth.

Serve over steamed or water-sautéed vegetables.
Use as a topping for a mixture of roasted red
pepper and steamed snow peas.

RED LENTIL SAUCE

serves: **4**

prep time: **30 minutes**

INGREDIENTS

½ cup dried red lentils

1 medium onion, chopped

1 clove garlic, chopped

1½ cups carrot juice

1 tablespoon
Dr. Fuhrman's VegiZest or
other no-salt seasoning

1 teaspoon ground cumin

1 teaspoon balsamic
vinegar

DIRECTIONS

Place the lentils, onions, garlic, and carrot juice
in a saucepan. Bring to a boil, cover, and
simmer for 20-30 minutes, until the lentils are soft
and pale.

Blend the cooked lentil mixture, VegiZest, cumin,
and vinegar in a food processor or high-
powered blender to a smooth purée.

Serve with steamed broccoli, cauliflower, or
other vegetables.

SESAME GINGER SAUCE

serves: **4**

prep time: **10 minutes**

INGREDIENTS

⅔ cup water

½ cup raw tahini

2 tablespoons fresh
lemon juice

1 teaspoon white miso,
low-sodium

1 tablespoon finely
grated fresh ginger

2 dates, pitted

1 clove garlic, pressed

pinch hot pepper flakes

DIRECTIONS

Blend all the ingredients in a food processor
or a high-powered blender. Add more water if
needed to achieve desired consistency.

Serve with steamed or water-sautéed vegetables.
This sauce goes well with bok choy, asparagus,
or kale.

SOUPS
AND
STEWS

APPLE CINNAMON BUTTERNUT SQUASH SOUP

INGREDIENTS

4 cups frozen butternut squash

2 medium apples, peeled, seeded, and chopped

4 cups (packed) chopped kale (stems and center ribs removed), or frozen kale

1 cup chopped onion

2 tablespoons Dr. Fuhrman's Pomegranate Vinegar or other fruit flavored vinegar

5 cups carrot juice

½ cup soy, almond, or hemp milk

½ cup raw cashews or ¼ cup raw cashew butter

1 teaspoon cinnamon

½ teaspoon nutmeg

DIRECTIONS

Place squash, apples, kale, onion, vinegar, and carrot juice in a soup pot. Bring to a boil, then lower heat, cover, and simmer for 30 minutes or until kale is very tender. Purée ½ of the soup with the milk and cashews in a food processor or high-powered blender. Return blended mixture to soup pot. Add cinnamon and nutmeg.

This soup is great as a warm and hearty winter breakfast. Make it the night before, refrigerate, and then reheat before serving.

BLACK FOREST CREAM OF MUSHROOM SOUP

serves: **5**

prep time: **40 minutes**

INGREDIENTS

2 tablespoons water

2 pounds mixed fresh mushrooms (such as button, shiitake, and cremini), cut into ¼-inch slices

2 cloves garlic, minced or pressed

2 teaspoons Herbes de Provence

5 cups carrot juice

3 cups unsweetened hemp, soy, or almond milk, divided

2 carrots, coarsely chopped

2 medium onions, chopped

¾ cup fresh or frozen corn kernels

1 cup chopped celery

3 leeks, cut in ½-inch rounds

¼ cup Dr. Fuhrman's VegiZest or other no-salt seasoning

¼ cup raw cashews

1 tablespoon fresh lemon juice

1 tablespoon chopped fresh thyme

2 teaspoons chopped fresh rosemary

3 cups cooked white beans (northern, navy, or cannellini), or 2 (15-ounce) cans, no-salt-added or low-sodium, rinsed and drained

5 ounces baby spinach

¼ cup chopped fresh parsley, for garnish

DIRECTIONS

Heat the water in a large sauté pan. Water sauté the mushrooms, garlic, and Herbes de Provence for about 5 minutes, or until tender, adding more water if necessary to prevent from sticking. Set aside.

In a large soup pot, bring the carrot juice, 2½ cups of the milk, carrots, onion, corn, celery, leeks, and VegiZest to a boil. Reduce heat and simmer until the vegetables are tender, about 30 minutes.

In a food processor or high-powered blender, purée the cashews and remaining ½ cup milk. Add half of the soup liquid and vegetables, the lemon juice, thyme, and rosemary. Blend until smooth and creamy.

Return the puréed soup mixture to the pot. Add the beans, spinach, and sautéed mushrooms. Heat until the spinach is wilted. Garnish with parsley.

"CHEESY" KALE SOUP

serves: **4**

prep time: **15 minutes**

INGREDIENTS

½ cup yellow split peas

1 onion, chopped

1 cup mushrooms, sliced

2 cups carrot juice

15 ounces tomato sauce, no-salt-added or low-sodium

1½ pounds chopped kale (stems and center ribs removed)

¼ cup cashew butter or ½ cup raw cashews

1 teaspoon nutritional yeast

DIRECTIONS

In a pressure cooker, cover yellow split peas with about 2½ cups of water and cook on high pressure for 6-8 minutes.

Add remaining ingredients except cashews and cook on high pressure for 1 minute. Release pressure and blend soup with cashews or cashew butter.

Sprinkle with nutritional yeast before serving.

To make without a pressure cooker, precook the split peas until soft. Combine cooked split peas with all remaining ingredients except cashews. Bring to a boil, reduce heat, and simmer until kale is tender (about 15 minutes). Add water as needed to achieve desired consistency. Blend in the cashews or mash and stir in cashew butter. Sprinkle with nutritional yeast before serving.

CREAMY BROCCOLI LENTIL SOUP

serves: **8**

prep time: **45 minutes**

INGREDIENTS

8 cups water

2 cups carrot juice, fresh or bottled

1 pound dried lentils

2 pounds organic plum tomatoes, chopped

4 cups broccoli, chopped

2 onions, chopped

3 celery stalks, chopped

2 carrots, chopped

6 cloves garlic, minced

3 small zucchini, chopped

1 tablespoon dried oregano

1½ teaspoons dried basil

1 teaspoon ground coriander

1 teaspoon ground cumin

1 teaspoon dried thyme

1 yam, chopped

3 tablespoons Dr. Fuhrman's Riesling Raisin Vinegar or balsamic vinegar

½ cup raw cashews

DIRECTIONS

Put all ingredients except yam, vinegar, and cashews in a large soup pot. Bring to a simmer and cook for 45 minutes. Add yam and simmer for an additional 15 minutes or until lentils and vegetables are tender.

Remove from heat. Add vinegar. Put 2 cups or more of soup and raw cashews into a food processor or high-powered blender and blend until very smooth. Stir back into soup.

CREAMY CRUCIFEROUS CURRY

serves: **4**

prep time: **30 minutes**

INGREDIENTS

2 onions, finely diced

4 cloves garlic, minced

3 carrots, diced

3 parsnips, diced

1 tablespoon curry powder

1 teaspoon turmeric

1 teaspoon cumin

2 cups soy, hemp, or almond milk

1 head cauliflower, cut into small florets

2 cups sliced mushrooms

1 pound chopped kale (stems and center ribs removed)

1 cup frozen green peas

2 cups cooked garbanzo beans (chickpeas), or 1 (15-ounce) can, no-salt-added or low-sodium, drained

½ cup raw almonds, lightly toasted and chopped

DIRECTIONS

In a large stock pot over medium heat, water sauté onions, garlic, carrots, and parsnips until onions are translucent (about 5 minutes). Add curry powder, turmeric, and cumin. Stir until vegetables are coated. Stir in soy milk, cauliflower, and mushrooms, cover, and cook over medium low heat for 10 minutes.

Stir in kale, green peas, and garbanzos, cover, and continue to cook for another 10 minutes. Top each serving with chopped toasted almonds.

DR. FUHRMAN'S FAMOUS ANTI-CANCER SOUP

serves: **10**

prep time: **20 minutes**

INGREDIENTS

1 cup dried split peas and/or beans

4 cups water

6-10 medium zucchini, cut into 1-inch pieces

5 pounds carrots, juiced (5-6 cups juice)*

2 bunches celery, juiced (2 cups juice)*

2 tablespoons Dr. Fuhrman's VegiZest or Mrs. Dash no-salt seasoning

4 medium onions, chopped

3 leek stalks, coarsely chopped

2 bunches kale, collard greens or other greens, chopped (stems and center ribs removed)

1 cup raw cashews

2½ cups fresh mushrooms (shiitake, cremini, and/or white), chopped

DIRECTIONS

Place the beans and water in a very large pot over low heat. Bring to a boil and simmer. Add the zucchini whole into the pot. Add the carrot juice, celery juice, and VegiZest. Put the onions, leeks, and kale in a blender and blend with a little bit of the soup liquid. Pour this mixture into the soup pot. Remove the softened zucchini with tongs and blend them in the blender with the cashews until creamy. Pour this mixture back into the soup pot. Add the mushrooms, and continue to simmer until the beans are soft, about 2 hours after they start to cook.

* Freshly juiced organic carrots and celery will maximize the flavor of this soup.

EASY THREE-BEAN VEGETABLE CHILI

serves: **6**

prep time: **30 minutes**

INGREDIENTS

1 pound firm tofu,
frozen, then defrosted

5 teaspoons chili powder,
or more to taste

1 teaspoon cumin

10 ounces frozen onions

3 cups frozen broccoli,
thawed and finely chopped

3 cups frozen cauliflower,
thawed and finely chopped

3 cloves garlic, chopped

1½ cups cooked pinto beans,
or 1 (15-ounce) can, no-salt-added
or low-sodium, rinsed and drained

1½ cups cooked black beans,
or 1 (15-ounce) can, no-salt-added
or low-sodium, rinsed and drained

1½ cups cooked red beans, or
1 (15-ounce) can, no-salt-added
or low-sodium, rinsed and drained

1 (28-ounce) can diced tomatoes,
no-salt-added or low-sodium

1 (4-ounce) can chopped
mild green chilies

2½ cups fresh or frozen
corn kernels

2 large zucchini, finely
chopped

DIRECTIONS

Squeeze excess water out of thawed tofu and crumble. Place the crumbled tofu, chili powder, and cumin in a soup pot and quickly brown. Add the remaining ingredients and simmer, covered, for 2 hours.

FAST BLACK BEAN SOUP

serves: **5**
prep time: **15 minutes**

INGREDIENTS

2 (15-ounce) cans black beans, no-salt-added or low-sodium, drained

2 cups frozen mixed vegetables

1½ cups frozen corn

2 cups frozen chopped broccoli florets

2 cups carrot juice

2 cups water

1 tablespoon chili powder, or to taste

1 teaspoon cumin

1 cup chopped fresh tomatoes

¼ cup chopped cilantro

1 avocado, chopped or mashed

½ cup chopped green onions

¼ cup raw pumpkin seeds

DIRECTIONS

Combine black beans, mixed vegetables, corn, broccoli, carrot juice, water, chili powder, and cumin in a soup pot. Bring to a boil and simmer on low for 30 minutes. Stir in fresh tomatoes and cilantro and heat through.

Serve topped with avocado, green onions, and pumpkin seeds.

For a creamy soup: After cooking, remove 2-3 cups of beans and vegetables, purée in a food processor or blender. Return the mixture to the pot. Add tomatoes and cilantro and heat through.

FRENCH MINTED PEA SOUP

serves: **3**

prep time: **20 minutes**

INGREDIENTS

10 ounces green peas, frozen

1 small onion, chopped

1 clove garlic, chopped

1 bunch fresh mint leaves (save a few leaves for garnish)

3 tablespoons Dr. Fuhrman's VegiZest or other no-salt soup base seasoning

3 cups water

3 dates, pitted

½ cup raw cashews

½ tablespoon Spike no-salt seasoning, or other no-salt seasoning, to taste

4 teaspoons fresh lemon juice

4 cups shredded romaine lettuce or chopped baby spinach

2 tablespoons freshly snipped chives

DIRECTIONS

Simmer peas, onions, garlic, mint, and VegiZest in water for about 7 minutes. Pour pea mixture into a high-powered blender or food processor. Add remaining ingredients except for the lettuce and chives. Blend until smooth and creamy. Add lettuce or spinach and let it wilt in the hot liquid.

Pour into bowls and garnish with chives and mint leaves.

GAZPACHO SUMMER SOUP

serves: **3**
prep time: **20 minutes**

INGREDIENTS

1 large cucumber, peeled and sliced into large pieces

1 large red bell pepper, seeded and sliced into large pieces

1½ cups diced tomatoes, or 1 (15-ounce) can, no-salt-added or low-sodium

1 cup roasted red peppers in vinegar, low-sodium, drained

2 cups tomato juice, no-salt-added or low-sodium

1 12-ounce jar mild or medium salsa, no-salt-added or low-sodium

½ cup fresh cilantro

2 tablespoons red wine vinegar

1 tablespoon Dr. Fuhrman's VegiZest

additional cucumber slices

DIRECTIONS

Place cucumbers and fresh red bell peppers in a food processor. Pulse until chopped in small pieces. Add tomatoes and roasted red peppers. Pulse again until finely chopped. Add tomato juice and remaining ingredients except cucumber slices and pulse until well mixed.

Cover and chill for at least 2 hours for flavors to mingle. Before serving, garnish with cucumber slices.

GOLDEN AUSTRIAN CAULIFLOWER SOUP

INGREDIENTS

1 head cauliflower, cut into pieces

3 carrots, coarsely chopped

1 cup coarsely chopped celery

2 leeks, coarsely chopped

2 cloves garlic, minced

2 tablespoons Dr. Fuhrman's VegiZest or other no-salt seasoning

2 cups carrot juice

4 cups water

1/2 teaspoon nutmeg

1 cup raw cashews

5 cups chopped kale leaves or baby spinach

DIRECTIONS

Place all the ingredients except the cashews and kale in a pot. Cover and simmer for 15 minutes or until the vegetables are just tender. Steam the kale until tender. If you are using spinach, there is no need to steam it; it will wilt in the hot soup.

In a food processor or high-powered blender, blend 2/3 of the soup liquid and vegetables with the cashews until smooth and creamy. Return the mixture to the pot and stir in the steamed kale (or raw spinach).

IN A HURRY
ANTI-CANCER SOUP

serves: **5**

prep time: **40 minutes**

INGREDIENTS

6 cups carrot juice*

3 large onions, chopped

5 large zucchini, cut into 1-inch pieces

2 cups mushrooms (any type), chopped

1 pound chopped kale (stems and center ribs removed)

1 pound mustard greens, chopped (stems removed)

1 teaspoon, no-sodium spice mix, such as Mrs. Dash no-salt seasoning

½ cup raw cashews or ¼ raw cashew butter

DIRECTIONS

Place all ingredients except cashews in a large stock pot. Bring to a boil, reduce heat to a simmer, cover, and cook for 30 minutes or until the vegetables are soft. Add cooked soup and cashews to a food processor or high-powered blender and blend until smooth and creamy. For a chunky soup, only blend a portion of the cooked soup with the cashews and then return the mixture to the pot.

* Use a good quality refrigerated carrot juice.

QUICK AND CREAMY VEGETABLE BEAN SOUP

serves: **8**

prep time: **15 minutes**

INGREDIENTS

4 cups prepared tomato soup, no-salt-added or low-sodium

2 cups frozen broccoli florets

2 cups frozen chopped spinach

2 cups carrot juice

1 cup chopped onions

4½ cups cooked cannellini beans, or 3 (15-ounce) cans, no-salt-added or low-sodium, drained

3 fresh tomatoes, chopped

1 bunch fresh basil, chopped

4 tablespoons Dr. Fuhrman's VegiZest or other no-salt seasoning, to taste

1 teaspoon garlic powder

½ teaspoon dried basil

½ teaspoon dried oregano

½ cup raw almonds

¼ cup pine nuts

DIRECTIONS

In soup pot, combine all ingredients except almonds and pine nuts. Cover and simmer for 30-40 minutes. In high-powered blender, blend ¼ of soup mixture with almonds. Add back to soup pot.

Serve with pine nuts sprinkled on top.

SOUTHWESTERN VEGETABLE STEW

serves: **3**

prep time: **20 minutes**

INGREDIENTS

1 large potato, cut into small pieces

½ medium green bell pepper, chopped

½ medium red bell pepper, chopped

½ medium onion, chopped

1-2 small jalapeno peppers, seeded and chopped

2 large cloves garlic, chopped

1½ tablespoons chili powder

1 (14-ounce) can chopped tomatoes, no-salt-added or low-sodium

1 cup fresh or frozen corn

1⅔ cups cooked black beans, or 1 (15-ounce) can, no-salt-added or low-sodium, drained

2 tablespoons chopped fresh cilantro

DIRECTIONS

Place potatoes in a pot and cover with water. Simmer for about 8 minutes until tender. Drain and set aside.

Heat ⅛ cup water in a large saucepan over medium heat. Add green and red peppers, onions, jalapenos, and garlic. Water sauté for 2 minutes. Add chili powder and stir for one minute. Add tomatoes, corn, beans, cilantro, and reserved potatoes. Simmer until potatoes are very tender, stirring occasionally, for about 10 minutes.

POTATO DOES NOT
NEED TO BE PEELED IF
ORGANIC

SPEEDY VEGETABLE AND BEAN SOUP

serves: **10**

prep time: **15 minutes**

INGREDIENTS

1 pound frozen Asian vegetables

1 pound frozen broccoli florets

1 pound frozen mixed vegetables

1 pound frozen collard greens

2 cups frozen corn

1 cup frozen onions

7 cups carrot juice

4 cups water

1½ cups sun-dried tomatoes, snipped in quarters

1 cup cooked adzuki beans or canned no-salt-added or low-sodium, drained

1 cup cooked red beans or canned no-salt-added or low-sodium, drained

3 cups cooked lentils or canned no-salt-added or low-sodium, drained

4 cloves garlic, chopped

4 tablespoons Dr. Fuhrman's VegiZest or other no-salt seasoning

1 tablespoon Spike no-salt seasoning

2 teaspoons chili powder

8 ounces organic baby spinach or coarsely chopped organic spinach

DIRECTIONS

In a large soup pot, combine all ingredients except the fresh spinach. Cover and simmer for 1 hour, stirring occasionally. Turn off heat and stir in spinach to wilt.

TUSCAN GREENS AND BEANS SOUP

serves: **6**

prep time: **30 minutes**

INGREDIENTS

1 cup sun-dried tomatoes

½ cup unsweetened soy, hemp, or almond milk

1 cup chopped onions

2 cloves garlic, minced

1 teaspoon dried basil

1 teaspoon dried oregano

½ teaspoon dried crushed rosemary

1½ cups cooked white beans, or 1 (15-ounce) can, no-salt-added or low-sodium, drained

1½ cups diced tomatoes, or 1 (15-ounce) can, no-salt-added or low-sodium, with liquid

3 cups vegetable broth, no-salt-added or low-sodium

1 cup water

6 cups chopped collard greens

1 tablespoon Dr. Fuhrman's Black Fig Vinegar or balsamic vinegar

½ teaspoon freshly ground black pepper

1 tablespoon Dr. Fuhrman's MatoZest or other no-salt seasoning blend

DIRECTIONS

Soak the sun-dried tomatoes in soy milk for one hour to soften. Drain, reserving soy milk. Chop tomatoes finely and set aside.

Heat ⅛ cup water over medium heat. Add onions and garlic and water sauté for 5 minutes, until onions are soft. If necessary, add more water to keep from sticking. Stir in sun-dried tomatoes, soy milk, basil, oregano, and rosemary.

Add the beans, diced tomatoes, vegetable broth, and water. Bring to a boil. Add the greens, lower heat, and simmer for about 20 minutes.

Before serving, stir in the vinegar, black pepper, and MatoZest

MAIN DISHES

ACORN SQUASH SUPREME

serves: **2**

prep time: **10 minutes**

INGREDIENTS

1 large acorn squash

4 tablespoons diced dried unsulfured apricots

1½ cups crushed pineapple and juice

2 tablespoons raisins

2 tablespoons chopped raw cashews

cinnamon

DIRECTIONS

Cut squash in half, remove seeds, and bake face-down in ½ inch of water for 45 minutes at 350°F.

Meanwhile, cover the apricots in a bowl with some of the pineapple juice. On top, add the pineapple, raisins, and cashews. Let stand and soak while the squash is cooking.

After the squash has cooked, mix the fruit and nut mixture in the bowl and scoop it into the squash's center. Place in pan and cover loosely with aluminum foil. Bake for an additional 30 minutes. Sprinkle with cinnamon, then put it back in the oven for 5 more minutes.

ARUGULA AND SPINACH STUFFED PITAS WITH WATERCRESS PESTO

INGREDIENTS

-SANDWICH-

4 whole grain pitas

1 tomato, sliced

½ cup sliced red onion

2 cups arugula

2 cups spinach

1 avocado, pit removed, sliced

-PESTO-

2 cups watercress, stems removed

5 basil leaves

½ cup walnuts

4 tablespoons unsweetened soy, hemp, or almond milk

DIRECTIONS

Prepare sandwiches with thinly sliced vegetables and finely shredded greens. Combine pesto ingredients in a high-powered blender until smooth. Spread on sandwiches.

ASIAN VEGETABLE STIR-FRY

serves: **4**

prep time: **45 minutes**

INGREDIENTS

14 ounces extra firm tofu, cubed

1 teaspoon Bragg Liquid Aminos or low-sodium soy sauce

¼ teaspoon crushed red pepper flakes

-SAUCE-

¼ cup unsulfured dried apricots soaked overnight in ½ cup water to cover

¼ cup unsalted natural peanut butter

2 tablespoons freshly chopped ginger

4 cloves garlic, chopped

-VEGETABLES-

2 tablespoons water

1 medium onion, cut into wedges and separated into 1-inch strips

4 cups small broccoli florets

2 medium carrots, cut diagonally into ⅓-inch pieces

4 medium red bell peppers, seeded and cut into 1-inch squares

1 cup sugar snap peas or snow peas, strings removed

2 tablespoons Spike no-salt seasoning or any other no-salt seasoning

½ cup brown rice

¼ cup unhulled sesame seeds

4 teaspoons Dr. Fuhrman's VegiZest or other no-salt seasoning

¼ cup Dr. Fuhrman's Black Fig Vinegar or balsamic vinegar

1 teaspoon arrowroot powder

¼ teaspoon crushed red pepper flakes

2 cups bok choy, cut in bite-sized pieces

3 cups fresh mushrooms (shiitake, porcini and/or cremini), stems removed

1 pound fresh spinach

½ cup raw cashews, coarsely chopped

1¼ pounds romaine lettuce, shredded

...continued

...continued

DIRECTIONS

Marinate the tofu for 30 minutes in the Liquid Aminos, red pepper flakes, and Spike. While the tofu marinates, cook the rice according to the package directions. Set aside.

Preheat the oven to 350°F. Toss the marinated tofu with the sesame seeds. Bake the sesame-coated tofu in a nonstick baking pan for 30-40 minutes, until golden.

To make the sauce, place all the ingredients in a food processor or high-powered blender and blend until smooth. Transfer to a small bowl and set aside.

Heat water in a large pan and water sauté the onion, broccoli, carrots, bell peppers, and peas for 5 minutes, adding more water as necessary to keep vegetables from scorching. Add the bok choy and mushrooms, cover, and simmer until the vegetables are just tender. Remove the cover and cook off most of the water. Add the spinach and toss until wilted.

Add the sauce and stir until all the vegetables are glazed and the sauce is hot and bubbly, about 1 minute. Mix in the cashews and baked tofu. Serve the stir-fry over the shredded lettuce along with ¼ cup brown rice per person.

Variation: Stir-fry beans or small pieces of chicken breast or shrimp with the vegetables.

BEAN ENCHILADAS

serves: **6**
prep time: **15 minutes**

INGREDIENTS

1 medium green bell pepper, seeded and chopped

½ cup sliced onion

8 ounces tomato sauce, divided, no-salt-added or low-sodium

2 cups cooked or canned no-salt-added or low-sodium pinto or black beans, drained and rinsed

1 cup frozen corn kernels

1 tablespoon chili powder

1 teaspoon ground cumin

1 teaspoon onion powder

1 tablespoon chopped fresh cilantro

⅛ teaspoon cayenne pepper, optional

6 corn tortillas

DIRECTIONS

Sauté the green pepper and onion in 2 tablespoons of the tomato sauce until tender. Stir in the remaining tomato sauce, beans, corn, chili powder, cumin, onion powder, cilantro, and cayenne (if using). Spoon about ¼ cup of the bean mixture on each tortilla and roll up.

Serve as is or bake for 15 minutes in a 375°F oven.

BETTER BURGERS

serves: **8**

prep time: **45 minutes**

INGREDIENTS

1½ cups old-fashioned rolled oats

1 cup ground walnuts

1 cup water

¼ cup tomato paste

¼ cup Dr. Fuhrman's MatoZest

1 cup onion, diced

3 cloves garlic, minced

6 cups mushrooms, finely minced

2 teaspoons dried basil

½ teaspoon dried oregano

2 tablespoons fresh parsley, minced

freshly ground pepper, to taste

⅔ cup frozen chopped spinach, thawed

DIRECTIONS

Preheat oven to 350°F.

Combine rolled oats and ground walnuts in a bowl. Set aside. In a small saucepan, whisk together water, tomato paste, and MatoZest and bring to a boil over medium heat. Pour over rolled oats and walnuts. Stir well and set aside.

Heat 2 tablespoons water in a sauté pan and add onion and garlic. Sauté until onion is translucent. Add mushrooms, basil, oregano, parsley, ground pepper, and additional water if needed, to prevent sticking. Cover and cook for 5 minutes, or until mushrooms are tender.

In a large bowl, combine sautéed onions and mushrooms, rolled oat/walnut mixture, and spinach. Stir well to combine. With wet hands, shape ⅓ cup of mixture into a well-formed burger. Place on a lightly oiled baking sheet and repeat with remaining mixture. Bake for 15 minutes. Turn burgers to bake the other side for another 15 minutes.

Remove from oven and cool slightly. Serve on small whole grain hamburger buns or whole grain pita bread halves. Top with thinly sliced, raw red onion and no-salt-added or low-sodium ketchup. Makes 12 burgers.

BLACK BEAN LETTUCE BUNDLES

INGREDIENTS

2 cups cooked or canned no-salt-added or low-sodium black beans, drained and rinsed

½ large ripe avocado, peeled and pitted

½ medium green bell pepper, seeded and chopped

3 green onions, chopped

⅓ cup chopped fresh cilantro

⅓ cup mild, no-salt-added or low-sodium salsa

2 tablespoons fresh lime juice

1 clove garlic, minced

1 teaspoon ground cumin

8 large romaine lettuce leaves

DIRECTIONS

In a bowl, mash the beans and avocado together with a fork until well blended and only slightly chunky. Add all the remaining ingredients except the lettuce, and mix.

Place approximately ¼ cup of the mixture in the center of each lettuce leaf and roll up like a burrito.

BRAISED KALE AND SQUASH WITH PUMPKIN SEEDS

serves: **6**

prep time: **40 minutes**

INGREDIENTS

2 bunches kale, chopped (stems and center ribs removed)

1 medium butternut squash or small pumpkin, peeled, seeded, and cubed

2 medium red onions, coarsely chopped

6 cloves garlic, sliced

2 tablespoons Dr. Fuhrman's VegiZest

⅔ cup water

3 tablespoons Dr. Fuhrman's Black Fig Vinegar or balsamic vinegar

1 cup raw pumpkin seeds or sunflower seeds, lightly toasted*

DIRECTIONS

Place kale, squash, onion, garlic, and VegiZest in a large pot with water. Cover and steam over low heat for 20 minutes or until kale and squash is tender. Add vinegar and toss. Serve sprinkled with lightly toasted pumpkin or sunflower seeds.

* Toast seeds in oven at 300°F for 4 minutes, or until lightly toasted.

BROCCOLI FRA DIAVOLO

serves: **2**

prep time: **10 minutes**

INGREDIENTS

5 cups fresh
broccoli florets

4 cloves garlic, chopped

1-½ cups diced fresh
tomatoes, or
1 (15-ounce) can,
no-salt-added

1 cup tomato or pasta
sauce, no-salt

dash dried hot
pepper flakes

1-2 teaspoons no-salt
Italian seasoning

¼ cup nutritional yeast

DIRECTIONS

Steam broccoli until tender. In large saucepan over medium heat, sauté garlic in ¼ cup water for 3-4 minutes. Add tomatoes, tomato sauce, hot pepper flakes, and Italian seasoning to taste. Simmer 10 minutes. Stir in broccoli and nutritional yeast.

BROCCOLI VINAIGRETTE

serves: **2**

prep time: **15 minutes**

INGREDIENTS

1 large head broccoli

¼ cup seasoned
rice vinegar

1 tablespoon
Dr. Fuhrman's VegiZest

2 teaspoons
Dijon mustard

2 large cloves garlic,
pressed or minced

DIRECTIONS

Chop broccoli into bite-sized florets. Peel stems and slice them into ¼-inch strips. Steam florets and stems for 8 minutes, or until just tender.

While the broccoli is steaming, whisk remaining ingredients in large bowl. Add broccoli and toss to mix.

BRUSSELS SPROUTS POLONAISE

serves: **3**

prep time: **10 minutes**

INGREDIENTS

6 cups brussels sprouts

¼ cup soft tofu

2 tablespoons lemon juice

2 dates, pitted

1 clove garlic, minced

1 tablespoon
Dr. Fuhrman's VegiZest

½ cup chopped fresh
parsley, divided

½ cup unsweetened soy,
hemp, or almond milk

DIRECTIONS

Cut large sprouts in half. Steam for 8 minutes until tender. Blend tofu, lemon juice, dates, garlic, VegiZest, ¼ cup parsley, and soy milk in blender and pour over sprouts. Sprinkle with remaining parsley.

CAULIFLOWER SPINACH MASHED "POTATOES"

serves: **4**

prep time: **25 minutes**

INGREDIENTS

6 cups cauliflower florets, fresh or frozen

4 cloves garlic, sliced

10 ounces fresh spinach

½ cup raw cashew butter

2 tablespoons Dr. Fuhrman's VegiZest or other no-salt seasoning

¼ teaspoon nutmeg

DIRECTIONS

Steam cauliflower and garlic about 8-10 minutes or until tender. Drain and press out as much water as possible in strainer. Place spinach in steamer, steam until just wilted, and set aside. Process cauliflower, garlic, and cashew butter in a food processor until creamy and smooth. If necessary, add a small amount of hemp or soy milk to thin consistency. Add VegiZest and nutmeg. Mix in wilted spinach.

CHUNKY SWEET POTATO STEW

serves: **2**

prep time: **25 minutes**

INGREDIENTS

1 onion, thickly sliced

2 large garlic cloves, chopped

1½ cups stewed tomatoes with juice, or 1 (15-ounce) can, no-salt-added or low-sodium

1 large sweet potato, peeled, cut into ½-inch pieces

½ cup cooked garbanzo beans (chickpeas) or white kidney beans

¾ teaspoon dried rosemary

1 medium zucchini, cut into ½-inch rounds

1 teaspoon Mrs. Dash no-salt seasoning

DIRECTIONS

In a sauté pan, heat 2 tablespoons water. Add the onion and water sauté about 5 minutes, until slightly softened, separating slices into rings. Add garlic and cook 1 minute. Add water as necessary to prevent from scorching.

Mix in stewed tomatoes with juice, sweet potatoes, garbanzo beans, and rosemary. Bring mixture to a simmer, stirring occasionally. Cover and cook 5 minutes. Add zucchini. Cover and cook until sweet potatoes are tender, about 15 minutes, stirring occasionally. Season with Mrs. Dash no-salt seasoning.

* *To make homemade stewed tomatoes: Place whole tomatoes in boiling water for 1 minute and then immediately transfer to cold water. Peel and quarter tomatoes, and place in a large saucepan. Slowly simmer over low heat for 20-30 minutes, stirring occasionally to prevent burning.*

CUBAN BLACK BEANS

serves: **6**
prep time: **20 minutes**

INGREDIENTS

1 cup chopped onion

¾ cup chopped green bell pepper

2 cups tomato juice, no-salt-added or low-sodium

4¼ cups cooked black beans, or 3 (15-ounce) cans, no-salt-added or low-sodium, drained

1½ cups chopped tomatoes, or 1 (15-ounce) can diced tomatoes, no-salt

1 cup tomato sauce, no-salt-added or low-sodium

3 cloves garlic, minced

1 tablespoon Dr. Fuhrman's VegiZest or other no-salt seasoning

½ teaspoon garlic powder

¼ teaspoon black pepper

DIRECTIONS

Heat 2 tablespoons water in a large pan and water sauté onions and peppers until tender. Add tomato juice and remaining ingredients. Bring to a boil, cover, reduce heat, and simmer 20-25 minutes or until vegetables are tender.

DELUXE SCRAMBLED TOFU

serves: **4**

prep time: **15 minutes**

INGREDIENTS

3 whole scallions, diced

½ cup red bell pepper, finely chopped

1 medium tomato, chopped

2 cloves garlic, minced or pressed

2 cups firm tofu, drained and crumbled

1 tablespoon Dr. Fuhrman's VegiZest or other no-salt seasoning

½ teaspoon Mrs. Dash no-salt seasoning, or more, to taste

1 tablespoon nutritional yeast, or more, to taste

5 ounces organic baby spinach, coarsely chopped

1 teaspoon Bragg Liquid Aminos

DIRECTIONS

In a large skillet, over medium/high heat, sauté scallions, red peppers, tomato, and garlic in ¼ cup water for 5 minutes. Add remaining ingredients and cook for another 5 minutes.

EASY RATATOUILLE

serves: **2**

prep time: **25 minutes**

INGREDIENTS

1 medium onion,
thinly sliced

2 garlic cloves, chopped

2 large tomatoes,
chopped, or 1 (15-ounce)
can diced tomatoes,
no-salt-added

1 medium eggplant,
cut into 1-inch dice

1 medium zucchini, cut
crosswise into 1-inch slices

1 medium red pepper,
cut into 1-inch pieces

1 teaspoon oregano

1 teaspoon basil

pepper (to taste)

DIRECTIONS

Heat ⅛ cup water in a large deep skillet. Water sauté the onion until softened, about 3 minutes. Add the garlic and cook for 1 minute, adding more water as necessary to keep from scorching. Reduce heat to moderately low and add the tomatoes, eggplant, zucchini, red pepper, and spices. Cover and cook, stirring occasionally until vegetables are very tender, about 1 hour.

Serve warm or at room temperature.

EASY VEGETABLE PIZZA

serves: **4**

prep time: **10 minutes**

INGREDIENTS

4 large whole grain pitas

2 cups pasta sauce, no-salt-added or low-sodium

½ cup chopped shiitake mushrooms

½ cup chopped red onion

10 ounces frozen broccoli florets, thawed and finely chopped

½ cup shredded non-dairy mozzarella-type cheese*

DIRECTIONS

Preheat the oven to 200°F.

Place pitas on two baking sheets and spoon on the pasta sauce. Sprinkle evenly with the mushrooms, onion, and broccoli. Add a light sprinkling of cheese. Bake for 20 minutes.

* *Daiya brand is a good choice.*

EGGPLANT STUFFED WITH TOFU PURÉE

serves: **4**

prep time: **60 minutes**

INGREDIENTS

1 cup shelled edamame, fresh or frozen

¼ cup firm tofu

⅓ cup water

4 tablespoons raw pumpkin seeds, toasted

½ teaspoon dried basil

½ teaspoon dried oregano

⅛ teaspoon black pepper

1 medium red bell pepper, coarsely chopped

1 medium onion, coarsely chopped

½ cup coarsely chopped carrots

4 cloves garlic, chopped

4 ounces baby spinach

2 medium eggplants, peeled and sliced lengthwise into ¼-inch slices

2 cups pasta sauce, no-salt-added or low-sodium

DIRECTIONS

Preheat oven to 350°F.

Boil edamame for 5 minutes. Combine in food processor with tofu, water, pumpkin seeds, basil, oregano, and black pepper. Set aside.

In ⅛ cup water, sauté red peppers, onions, carrots, and garlic until tender, adding more water if needed. Add spinach and cook until wilted. Set aside.

Roast eggplant in baking pan lightly oiled with olive oil for about 20 minutes or until tender and flexible enough to roll up.

In baking pan, spread about ¼ cup tomato sauce. Place 1-2 tablespoons edamame purée in center of each eggplant slice. Top with sautéed vegetable mixture. Roll up and place in baking dish, seam side down. Top with remaining sauce.

Bake 20-30 minutes or until heated through.

GARDEN STUFFED VEGETABLES

INGREDIENTS

½ cup quinoa, rinsed well

2 medium zucchini, cut in half lengthwise, seeds and some meat removed, leaving shells intact

4 large peppers, assorted colors, tops sliced off, seeds removed

2 medium Portobello mushrooms, stems removed

1 small red bell pepper, chopped

½ pound shiitake mushrooms, chopped

3 whole green onions, chopped

2 stalks celery, chopped

1 stalk broccoli, chopped in small pieces

4 cloves garlic, chopped in small pieces

1 cup cooked lentils, or
1 (15-ounce) can, no-salt-added or low-sodium, drained

½ cup walnuts, coarsely chopped

2 ounces non-dairy mozzarella type cheese*, shredded

½ cup raisins

¼ cup plus 2 tablespoons parsley, chopped, divided

1 tablespoon Dr. Fuhrman's VegiZest or other no-salt seasoning

2 cups pasta sauce, no-salt-added or low-sodium

salad greens

1 tablespoon Dr. Fuhrman's Black Fig Vinegar or balsamic vinegar

DIRECTIONS

Preheat oven to 350°F. Cook quinoa in 1-½ cups water for 20 minutes and set aside. Bake the zucchini and peppers on a rimmed baking sheet for 5 minutes. Add Portobello mushrooms and bake for an additional 15 minutes.

Heat ⅛ cup of water in a large pan and water sauté chopped red bell pepper, shiitake mushrooms, green onions, celery, broccoli, and garlic until tender and water has cooked off. In large bowl, mix cooked quinoa, lentils, walnuts, non-dairy cheese, raisins, and ¼ cup chopped parsley with sautéed ingredients and season with VegiZest. Fill zucchini, mushrooms, and peppers with quinoa mixture and place in a baking dish. Spoon pasta sauce over vegetables. Bake for 20 minutes until hot.

Serve on bed of salad greens which have been lightly tossed with Dr. Fuhrman's Black Fig vinegar or balsamic vinegar. Garnish vegetables with remaining chopped parsley.

Daiya brand cheese substitute is a good choice.

GREAT GREENS

serves: **4**

prep time: **15 minutes**

INGREDIENTS

1 large bunch kale, chopped (stems and center ribs removed)

1 bunch Swiss chard, chopped (stems removed)

1 tablespoon Dr. Fuhrman's Spicy Pecan Vinegar or other flavored vinegar

1 clove garlic, minced

½ tablespoon Dr. Fuhrman's VegiZest or other no-salt seasoning

1 teaspoon dried dill

1 teaspoon dried basil

black pepper to taste

DIRECTIONS

Steam the kale for 10 minutes. Add the Swiss chard and steam for another 10 minutes or until tender. Transfer to a bowl. Combine the remaining ingredients and add to the greens. If desired, add 2-3 tablespoons of the steaming water to adjust consistency.

HERBED BARLEY AND LENTILS

serves: **4**

prep time: **10 minutes**

INGREDIENTS

½ cup chopped onions

2 cloves garlic, chopped

1 cup hulled barley*

¼ cup lentils

3 cups water

½ teaspoon Italian seasoning

1 tablespoon finely chopped fresh chives (or 1 teaspoon dried)

2 tablespoons finely chopped fresh basil (or ½ teaspoon dried)

DIRECTIONS

In a large saucepan, water sauté onions and garlic in a small amount of water until soft. Add remaining ingredients and bring to a boil. Reduce heat, cover, and simmer for 1 hour or until barley and lentils are tender and water is absorbed.

* Hulled barley is barley that has been minimally processed to remove only the tough, inedible outer hull. Pearled barley receives additional processing and has a lower nutritional value.

KALE PESTO OVER PASTA AND BEANS

serves: **6**

prep time: **30 minutes**

INGREDIENTS

6 ounces whole wheat or brown rice penne pasta

1 bunch kale, chopped (stems and center ribs removed)

½ cup pine nuts, lightly toasted*

5 cloves garlic, minced

¼ cup unsweetened soy, hemp, or almond milk

1 tablespoon fresh lemon juice

6 cups organic baby spinach

¼ teaspoon crushed red pepper flakes

3 cups cooked cannellini beans, or 2 (15-ounce) cans, no-salt-added or low-sodium, drained

DIRECTIONS

Cook pasta according to package directions. Steam kale until tender. Pat with a paper towel to remove excess moisture. In a food processor, combine steamed kale, pine nuts, garlic, soy milk, and lemon juice until a thick pesto is formed. Heat ⅛ cup water in a large skillet, add spinach and red pepper flakes and heat for 3 minutes or until spinach is soft. Add pesto. Mix pasta and beans. Pour sauce over top.

* Lightly toast pine nuts in a pan over medium heat for 4 minutes, shaking pan frequently.

KALE WITH CASHEW CREAM SAUCE

serves: **4**

prep time: **15 minutes**

INGREDIENTS

2 large bunches of kale, stems and center ribs removed

½ cup raw cashews

1 cup hemp, soy, or almond milk

¼ cup onion flakes

1 tablespoon Dr. Fuhrman's VegiZest or other no-salt seasoning (optional)

DIRECTIONS

Steam the kale for 15 minutes or until tender. Meanwhile, blend the cashews, milk, onion flakes, and VegiZest in a food processor or high-powered blender until smooth and creamy.

When the kale is done, press it between a clean dish towel to remove any excess water, chop, and mix with the sauce.

LEMON ZEST SPINACH

serves: **4**

prep time: **10 minutes**

INGREDIENTS

1 ¼ pounds fresh
organic spinach or
4 bags organic baby
spinach

6 cloves garlic, minced

5 tablespoons pine nuts,
lightly toasted*

3 teaspoons lemon juice

DIRECTIONS

Steam spinach and garlic until spinach is just
wilted. Place in bowl and toss with pine nuts and
lemon juice.

* Lightly toast pine nuts in a pan over medium
  heat for 4 minutes, shaking pan frequently.

MEDITERRANEAN BEAN AND KALE SAUTÉ

serves: **4**

prep time: **20 minutes**

INGREDIENTS

2 bunches chopped kale
(stems and center ribs removed)

½ cup sun-dried tomatoes,
soaked in hot water for 30 minutes,
drained and chopped

1 medium onion, finely chopped

1 cup shiitake mushrooms,
coarsely chopped

3 cloves garlic, pressed

1 tablespoon Dr. Fuhrman's
VegiZest, or other no-salt
seasoning blend

1 cup cooked beans (any type),
or 1 (15-ounce) can, no-salt-added
or low-sodium

1-½ tablespoons Dr. Fuhrman's
Riesling Raisin Vinegar or other
fruity vinegar

1 tablespoon Dijon mustard

red pepper flakes, to taste

½ cup pasta sauce, no-salt-added
or low-sodium,

¼ cup pine nuts, almonds, or
any type raw chopped nuts

⅛ cup non-dairy Parmesan cheese

DIRECTIONS

Heat ⅛ cup water in a large skillet, and water sauté the kale, tomatoes,
onion, mushrooms, and garlic over medium heat for 5 minutes, adding
additional water as needed. Add VegiZest, cover, and steam for 10
minutes. Add the beans, vinegar, mustard, and red pepper flakes, and
cook for 3 more minutes or until mushrooms are tender and liquid cooks
out. Toss with pasta sauce. Serve topped with chopped nuts and non-
dairy Parmesan cheese.

MUSHROOM STROGANOFF

serves: **4**

prep time: **20 minutes**

INGREDIENTS

2 medium onions, chopped

1 clove garlic, minced

1 pound mushrooms, thinly sliced

2 tablespoons fresh lemon juice

1 tablespoon fresh tarragon, chopped, or 1 teaspoon dried tarragon

1 tablespoon sweet paprika

1 cup vegetable broth, no-salt-added or low-sodium

2 tablespoons tahini or puréed unhulled sesame seeds

DIRECTIONS

In a nonstick skillet, water sauté onion and garlic until soft. Add mushrooms and continue cooking until mushrooms soften and lose their moisture. Add lemon juice, tarragon, and paprika and mix well. Blend vegetable broth and tahini. (Heating the broth makes blending easier.) Pour over mushroom mixture and mix well. Simmer until mixture thickens slightly or until desired consistency.

Variations: Mushroom Stroganoff can be served over a bed of steamed kale, spinach, smashed steamed cauliflower, parsnips, or baked potato.

NO-MEAT BALLS

serves: **6**

prep time: **40 minutes**

INGREDIENTS

1 cup diced onion

3 cloves garlic, roasted and mashed

¼ cup diced celery

2 tablespoons minced fresh parsley

¼ teaspoon dried sage

1 teaspoon dried basil

1 teaspoon dried oregano

1½ cup cooked lentils, or 1 (15-ounce) can, no-salt-added or low-sodium, drained and rinsed

¼ cup cooked brown rice

2-3 tablespoons tomato paste

1 tablespoon arrowroot powder or whole wheat flour

2 tablespoons Dr. Fuhrman's MatoZest or other no-salt seasoning

2 tablespoons nutritional yeast

freshly ground black pepper to taste

2 tablespoons vital wheat gluten flour for a chewier consistency (optional)

DIRECTIONS

Preheat oven to 350°F.

In a sauté pan, heat 1 tablespoon water. Add the onion and garlic and sauté for 5 minutes. Add the celery, parsley, sage, basil, and oregano. Sauté for another 5 minutes, adding more water as needed to prevent sticking. In a large bowl, combine the sautéed vegetables with the remaining ingredients and mix well. Mash lightly with a potato masher.

With wet hands, form 2 tablespoons of the mashed mixture into a smooth ball. Repeat. Place the balls on a very lightly oiled baking sheet and bake for 20 minutes. Serve with your favorite no-salt-added or low-sodium marinara sauce.

Makes 18 balls.

NO-PASTA VEGETABLE LASAGNA

serves: **8**

prep time: **60 minutes**

INGREDIENTS

-LASAGNA "NOODLES"-

2 large eggplants, sliced lengthwise into ¼-inch slices

3 small zucchini, sliced lengthwise as thinly as possible

3 small yellow squash, sliced lengthwise as thinly as possible

-TOFU RICOTTA-

16 ounces silken tofu

1 small onion, cut into quarters

4 cloves garlic, cut in half

1 cup fresh basil leaves

1¼ pounds firm tofu, squeezed dry and crumbled

¼ cup Dr. Fuhrman's VegiZest

2 tablespoons dried Italian herbs

1 cup grated non-dairy mozzarella cheese*

-VEGETABLES-

2 heads broccoli, coarsely chopped

4 cups sliced mixed fresh mushrooms (shiitake, cremini, oyster)

4 medium bell peppers (red, yellow, and/or orange), seeded and chopped

7 ounces baby spinach

3 cups pasta sauce, no-salt-added or low-sodium, divided

shredded fresh basil for garnish

DIRECTIONS

To make the lasagna noodles, preheat the oven to 350°F. Wipe a baking pan with a small amount of olive oil. Place the eggplant, zucchini, and yellow squash in the pan and bake for 10 minutes, or until flexible but not completely cooked. Work in batches if necessary. Set aside.

...continued

...continued

NO-PASTA VEGETABLE LASAGNA

While the "noodles" are baking, make the tofu "ricotta." Purée the silken tofu, onion, and garlic in a food processor or high-powered blender. Add the basil leaves and pulse to coarsely chop. Transfer to a medium bowl and mix in the crumbled firm tofu. Add the VegiZest, Italian seasoning, and grated non-dairy cheese. Set aside.

To prepare the vegetables, sauté broccoli, mushrooms, bell peppers, and spinach without water, over low heat for 5 minutes, stirring constantly, until tender.

To assemble the lasagna, spread a thin layer of the pasta sauce on the bottom of a baking dish. Layer the eggplant slices, sautéed vegetables, yellow squash slices, zucchini slices, and tofu "ricotta," and then spread with pasta sauce. Repeat the layers, ending with the tofu "ricotta." Spread the remaining pasta sauce on top and bake at 350°F, uncovered, for 1 hour, or until hot and bubbly. Garnish with the shredded basil.

* Daiya brand is a good choice.

INGREDIENTS

8 ounces tempeh, thinly sliced diagonally

1 pound shiitake mushrooms, stemmed, thinly sliced

-MARINADE-

2 cloves garlic, minced

1 tablespoon chopped fresh basil

1 tablespoon chopped fresh cilantro

pinch hot pepper flakes

1 cup vegetable broth, low-sodium

2 tablespoons balsamic vinegar

1 teaspoon Braggs Liquid Aminos or low-sodium soy sauce

-CRUST-

1 cup pistachios, shelled

4 tablespoons corn meal

2 tablespoons nutritional yeast

1 teaspoon onion powder

1 teaspoon garlic powder

PISTACHIO CRUSTED TEMPEH WITH BALSAMIC MARINADE AND SHIITAKE MUSHROOMS

DIRECTIONS

Place tempeh in a saucepan with water to cover, simmer for 10 minutes.

Combine ingredients for marinade. Remove tempeh from water and add to marinade. Marinate for at least one hour.

Preheat oven to 400°F. Process pistachios in food processor until finely chopped. Add remaining crust ingredients and pulse until thoroughly mixed. Place in large shallow bowl. Remove tempeh from marinade and drain reserving marinade. Dip tempeh in crust mixture to coat.

Place crusted tempeh and sliced mushrooms side by side on a rimmed baking sheet. Spoon 2-3 tablespoons of marinade over mushrooms. Bake for 13 minutes or until mushrooms are soft, turning occasionally.

Simmer remaining marinade for 2 minutes. Drizzle tempeh and mushrooms with marinade before serving.

PORTOBELLO
MUSHROOMS AND BEANS

serves: **4**

prep time: **10 minutes**

INGREDIENTS

1 large onion, chopped

2 garlic cloves, chopped

2 large Portobello
mushroom caps, sliced thin

½ cup red wine
(or low-sodium
vegetable broth)

1 large tomato, diced, or
8 halved cherry tomatoes

1½ cups cooked
garbanzo beans
(chickpeas), or
1 (15-ounce) can,
no-salt-added or
low-sodium, drained

DIRECTIONS

Water sauté the onion and garlic for 2 minutes
or until onions are soft. Add the mushrooms and
the red wine or broth and continue cooking for
5 minutes, until mushrooms are tender. Add the
tomatoes and garbanzo beans. Simmer for 5
minutes.

PORTOBELLO
RED PEPPER SANDWICH

serves: **4**

prep time: **25 minutes**

INGREDIENTS

-SANDWICH-

4 large Portobello
mushrooms, stems removed

1 large red onion,
thinly sliced

4 whole grain pitas

2 cups large arugula
leaves

2 medium drained roasted
red bell peppers, from
jar, seeded and cut into
½-inch slices

-TAHINI SPREAD-

¾ cup tahini or 1 cup
unhulled sesame seeds

½ cup water

1 tablespoon fresh
lemon juice

1 tablespoon Dr. Fuhrman's
VegiZest or other no-salt
seasoning blend, to taste

2 pitted dates, chopped

1 small clove garlic,
chopped

DIRECTIONS

Preheat oven to 375°F.

Arrange mushrooms and onions on baking sheet
and roast until tender, about 15-20 minutes.
Meanwhile, make tahini spread by blending
all ingredients together until creamy in a food
processor or high-powered blender. (If using
whole sesame seeds, blend sesame seeds with
¼ cup of water until creamy and then add the
other ¼ cup water and remaining ingredients.)

When mushrooms and onions are done, split
pitas in half horizontally and warm slightly.
Spread generous amount of tahini spread on top
half of split pita. Place ½ cup arugula on bottom
half and then 1 mushroom cap (pat dry with
paper towels to absorb liquid), sliced onion, and
roasted red pepper.

QUICK VEGETABLE BEAN MEDLEY

serves: **4**

prep time: **15 minutes**

INGREDIENTS

1 head broccoli, small florets, stems peeled and sliced into ½-inch pieces

1 red bell pepper, thinly sliced

8 cloves garlic, chopped

½ pound shiitake mushrooms, sliced

3 cups cooked red beans, or 2 (15-ounce) cans, no-salt-added or low-sodium, drained

1 tablespoon Dr. Fuhrman's VegiZest or other no-salt seasoning

½ cup sunflower seeds, lightly toasted

DIRECTIONS

In large pan, heat ⅛ cup water. Add broccoli, red pepper, garlic, and mushrooms; cover and sauté vegetables until tender, about 10 minutes. Add beans and VegiZest and continue cooking, uncovered, for an additional 5 minutes, adding more water if necessary. Top with sunflower seeds.

ROASTED VEGETABLE PIZZA

serves: **2**

prep time: **25 minutes**

INGREDIENTS

2 cups broccoli florets

1 large red bell pepper, cut into 1-inch slices

1 large Portobello mushroom, cut into ½-inch slices

1 teaspoon garlic powder

1 tablespoon balsamic vinegar

1 teaspoon Mrs. Dash no-salt seasoning or Spike no-salt seasoning

5 ounces organic baby spinach

2 whole grain tortillas

½ cup pasta sauce, no-salt-added or low-sodium

2 ounces mozzarella-type non-dairy cheese

DIRECTIONS

Preheat oven to 350°F.

Toss broccoli, bell peppers, and mushrooms with garlic powder, balsamic vinegar, and seasoning. Roast seasoned vegetables on a cookie sheet for 30 minutes, turning occasionally, and mounding to keep from drying out.

Steam spinach until just wilted.

Preheat oven to 450°F. Spread a thin layer of pasta sauce on tortillas, distribute roasted vegetables and spinach on top, and sprinkle with non-dairy cheese.

Bake for approximately 7 minutes or until cheese is melted and tortillas are lightly browned around edges.

SHIITAKE BROCCOLI QUICHE

serves: **6**
prep time: **30 minutes**

INGREDIENTS

-PIE SHELL-

1½ cups raw cashews

1 cup walnuts

½ cup raw
sunflower seeds

1 cup water

½ cup shredded
unsweetened coconut

⅓ cup raisins

¼ cup raw cashew butter

-QUICHE FILLING-

1 teaspoon olive oil

1 medium onion, diced

1 head broccoli, chopped

1 cup chopped shiitake
mushrooms

1 package firm tofu,
drained and squeezed

1 tablespoon dried basil

½ teaspoon turmeric

¼ teaspoon nutmeg

1 tablespoon Dr. Fuhrman's
Black Fig Vinegar

½ cup unsweetened soy,
hemp, or almond milk

DIRECTIONS

-PIE SHELL-
Blend cashews, walnuts, and sunflower seeds
with water in a high-powered blender until
creamy. Add coconut, raisins, and cashew
butter. Blend until smooth and creamy. Spread
and press into pie dish.

Bake at 350°F for 30 minutes, remove from
oven, but leave the oven on.

-QUICHE FILLING-
Heat the olive oil in a medium saucepan over
medium heat. Using a spray bottle of water,
sauté the onion, broccoli, and mushrooms until
tender, about 6-8 minutes, adding water to the
pan as needed to prevent sticking and burning.
In a blender or food processor, blend the tofu,
basil, turmeric, nutmeg, vinegar, and soy milk
until smooth. Remove from blender and combine
with broccoli mixture.

Pour into pie shell. Bake for 20 minutes or until
pie is thickened.

SPAGHETTI SQUASH PRIMAVERA

serves: **4**

prep time: **20 minutes**

INGREDIENTS

1 medium spaghetti squash

1½ carrots, diagonally sliced

½ cup organic celery, diagonally sliced

3 cloves garlic, minced

1½ cups shredded cabbage

1 small zucchini, chopped into small pieces

1½ cups cooked pinto beans, or 1 (15-ounce) can, no-salt-added or low-sodium, drained

1½ cups chopped tomatoes, or 1 (15-ounce) can diced tomatoes, no-salt-added or low-sodium, drained

⅓ cup vegetable broth, no-salt-added or low-sodium

1 teaspoon dried thyme

1 teaspoon dried parsley

1 cup pasta sauce, no-salt-added or low-sodium

1 head romaine lettuce leaves

DIRECTIONS

Preheat oven to 350°F.

Slice spaghetti squash in half lengthwise; remove seeds. Place both halves upside down on a baking sheet. Bake for 45 minutes, or until tender. Meanwhile, cook carrots and celery in 2 tablespoons of water in a covered pan over medium heat for 10 minutes, stirring occasionally. Add a little more water if needed. Add garlic, cabbage, and zucchini. Cook, covered, for another 10 minutes. Stir in beans, tomatoes, vegetable broth, thyme, and parsley. Cover and simmer for another 10 minutes, or until carrots are tender.

When squash is done, remove from oven. Using a fork, scrape spaghetti-like strands from squash into a bowl. Add pasta sauce and combine by mixing thoroughly. Mix the vegetables and beans with the squash/pasta sauce mixture and serve on a bed of shredded romaine lettuce, if desired, or place back in the hollowed-out squash bowls.

SPEEDY VEGETABLE WRAP

serves: **2**
prep time: **12 minutes**

INGREDIENTS

2 whole grain tortillas
or whole grain pitas

1 tablespoon fat-free
dressing, divided for
½ tablespoon per wrap

2 cups broccoli slaw mix

1 large tomato, diced

2 tablespoons non-dairy
cheese, shredded

DIRECTIONS

Spread fat-free dressing over tortillas. Add broccoli slaw mix, tomatoes, and non-dairy cheese. Place in toaster oven or microwave just long enough to melt the cheese. Roll up tortillas, enclosing filling. If making pitas, stuff with dressing, vegetable, and cheese, and serve without heating.

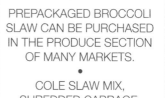

PREPACKAGED BROCCOLI
SLAW CAN BE PURCHASED
IN THE PRODUCE SECTION
OF MANY MARKETS.
·
COLE SLAW MIX,
SHREDDED CABBAGE,
OR SHREDDED BROCCOLI
ALSO MAY BE USED

SPINACH FALAFEL WITH TAHINI

serves: **6**

prep time: **30 minutes**

INGREDIENTS

-FALAFEL-

2 tablespoons ground flaxseed

¼ cup unhulled sesame seeds

1½ cups cooked garbanzo beans (chickpeas), or 1 (15-ounce) can, no-salt-added or low-sodium, drained

1 onion, diced

2 cloves garlic, minced

2 tablespoons fresh parsley, chopped

-TAHINI SAUCE-

4 tablespoons tahini or unhulled sesame seeds

12 ounces firm silken tofu

1 tablespoon lemon juice

⅛ teaspoon black pepper, or to taste

¼ teaspoon paprika

½ teaspoon cumin

2 teaspoons Dr. Fuhrman's VegiZest

½ cup plus 2 tablespoons garbanzo bean (chickpea) flour*

10-ounce package frozen spinach, thawed and drained

1 tablespoon lemon juice

1 clove garlic, peeled, chopped

⅛ teaspoon pepper, or to taste

DIRECTIONS

Grind flaxseed and sesame seeds in a coffee grinder or food processor.

Put garbanzos, ground flaxseed, and ground sesame seeds in a food processor and combine until smooth. Add onion, garlic, parsley, lemon juice, black pepper, paprika, cumin, and VegiZest to bean mixture and blend until combined. Add garbanzo bean flour and process again, until evenly distributed. Bean mixture should be smooth and thick; it will ball up in the processor.

Press thawed spinach into a colander. Place bean mixture into a separate bowl and slowly add the spinach to the bean mixture. Mix with spatula just until spinach is evenly distributed.

...continued

...*continued*

SPINACH FALAFEL
WITH TAHINI

Form mixture into six burgers, using about a half cup of batter for each patty. Place on nonstick, lightly oiled cookie sheet and bake at 350°F for 25 minutes. Turn over each patty, and bake for another 15 minutes. Allow burgers to cool 10 minutes before serving.

To make tahini sauce, process all sauce ingredients in a food processor or high-powered blender until smooth. If using sesame seeds instead of tahini, grind seeds prior to adding other ingredients.

Enjoy falafels with lettuce, tomato, and tahini sauce alone or with a whole wheat pita.

* *Garbanzo bean flour can be found in health food markets and in supermarkets in the gluten-free or health food section.*

STUFFED ARTICHOKES

serves: **4**

prep time: **20 minutes**

INGREDIENTS

4 medium artichokes

3 stalks fresh basil leaves

1 cup walnuts

½ cup unsweetened soy, hemp, or almond milk

1 teaspoon dried oregano

1 teaspoon garlic powder

DIRECTIONS

Preheat oven to 350°F.

Trim the stems from the artichokes, and remove the small leaves from the bottoms. Slice artichoke up the middle through stem and top to expose triangular choke. Using a small sharp knife, cut out the small choke center along the fuzz border and discard. Steam for about 15 minutes, until a leaf can be pulled off.

In a food processor, mix together the basil, walnuts, soy milk, and oregano. Spoon the mixture into artichoke bowl. Sprinkle with garlic powder.

Bake for 15 minutes.

SUPER LENTIL LOAF

serves: **6**

prep time: **45 minutes**

INGREDIENTS

2 large artichokes, rinsed

½ cup diced onion

2 cloves garlic, minced

3 cups finely chopped mushrooms

¼ cup diced celery

2 tablespoons minced parsley

½ teaspoon poultry seasoning

1½ cups cooked lentils, or 1 (15-ounce) can lentils, no-salt-added or low-sodium, rinsed and drained

⅓ cup finely chopped raw pecans

¼ cup rolled oats

¼ cup tomato paste (divided)

2 tablespoons arrowroot powder (or whole wheat flour)

2 tablespoons MatoZest

freshly ground black pepper, to taste

DIRECTIONS

Preheat oven to 350°F.

Slice one inch off the top of each artichoke. Cut off the very bottom of the stem, but keep the stems attached. Slice artichokes in half, lengthwise. Place them in a steamer basket over several inches of water. Bring water to a boil, cover, and steam for 40 minutes. Set artichokes aside until cool enough to handle. Scoop out and discard the fibrous choke from the center of each artichoke. Remove the hearts and transfer to a bowl. Mash lightly. Scrape off the bottom one third of each leaf and add to mashed hearts. Carefully scrape out the tender insides of the stems to use as well.

In a sauté pan, heat one tablespoon of water or vegetable broth. Add onion and garlic and sauté for 5 minutes. Add mushrooms, cover, and cook until mushrooms are tender. Add celery, parsley, and poultry seasoning. Sauté another 5 minutes, adding more water if needed to prevent sticking.

Place the sautéed vegetables in a bowl and add the lentils, 1 cup of mashed artichokes, pecans, oats, tomato paste, arrowroot powder, MatoZest, and black pepper. Stir well to combine.

Lightly rub a loaf pan with minimal amount of oil. Fill the loaf pan with the lentil mixture and press down evenly. Spread ⅛-inch layer of reserved tomato paste over top. Bake for 1 hour. Remove from oven and let stand at room temperature for 30 minutes before slicing and serving.

SUPREME KALE

INGREDIENTS

1 small onion, sliced thin

1 clove garlic, chopped

¼ teaspoon crushed red pepper flakes

1 bunch kale, chopped (stems and center ribs removed)

2 carrots, shredded or sliced thin with a vegetable peeler

1 tablespoon toasted sesame seeds

DIRECTIONS

In a large pan, water sauté onion, garlic, and red pepper flakes for 1 minute. Add half of the kale and stir for 1 minute. Add the remaining kale and cook until softened. Use a small amount of water as needed to prevent sticking. Add shredded carrots and continue cooking 2-4 minutes until kale is tender.

Toss with sesame seeds.

serves: **6**

prep time: **25 minutes**

INGREDIENTS

2 medium sweet potatoes, peeled and chopped into bite-sized pieces

6 dried figs, chopped

12 ounces baby spinach

2 cups water

2 tablespoons Dr. Fuhrman's VegiZest, or other no-sodium soup-base seasoning

2 large leeks, white and pale green parts only, washed thoroughly and cut into ½-inch slices

1 clove garlic, minced

1 pound fresh asparagus, trimmed and cut diagonally into 1-inch pieces

7 ounces fresh shiitake mushrooms, chopped

1 tablespoon fresh lemon juice

3 tablespoons chopped fresh parsley

2 tablespoons chopped fresh mint leaves

2 tablespoons chopped raw Brazil nuts, or other raw nuts, if desired

SWEET POTATO AND ASPARAGUS RAGOUT

DIRECTIONS

Place potatoes and figs in a steamer and steam until potatoes are tender, about 10 minutes. Add spinach on top of potatoes in the steamer, cover, and allow to wilt. Once spinach is wilted, transfer mixture into a bowl and set aside.

In a skillet, mix water and VegiZest. Add leeks, garlic, and asparagus. Cover and simmer until leeks and asparagus are tender, about 10 minutes. Remove with a slotted spoon and transfer to the bowl with potatoes and spinach.

In the same skillet, sauté mushrooms, stirring occasionally, until mushrooms are softened, about 2 minutes. Add mushrooms to potato, spinach, and asparagus mixture. Add lemon juice, parsley, mint, and nuts, and gently toss.

SWEET POTATO FRIES

serves: **4**

prep time: **10 minutes**

INGREDIENTS

4 sweet potatoes

1 tablespoon
garlic powder

1 tablespoon
onion powder

DIRECTIONS

Preheat oven to 400°F.

Peel sweet potatoes if not organic. Cut into strips. Lay on a nonstick cookie sheet. Sprinkle garlic powder and onion powder on potatoes. Bake approximately 90 minutes, turning potatoes every 15 minutes.

serves: **6**

Prep time: **30 minutes**

SWISS CHARD AND SWEET POTATO GRATIN

INGREDIENTS

1 teaspoon chopped fresh ginger

1 onion, finely chopped

½ cup chopped green pepper

8 cups Swiss chard, coarsely chopped (stems removed)

4 medium (about 1-¼ pounds) sweet potatoes, peeled, cut into ⅛-inch slices

8 ounces tempeh, sliced very thin

2 cups unsweetened hemp, soy, or almond milk

⅛ teaspoon nutmeg

⅛ teaspoon black pepper

¼ cup non-dairy mozzarella cheese

2 tablespoons flaxseed, toasted

DIRECTIONS

Preheat oven to 400 F.

Rub a 9"x13" baking dish with a small amount of olive oil. Heat ⅛ cup water in a large pan and water sauté ginger, onion, and green pepper until softened. Add Swiss chard and cook until just tender.

In the prepared baking dish, build layers as follows. Arrange a third of the sliced sweet potatoes on the bottom. Top with half of the tempeh and half of the Swiss chard mixture. Add another third of the sweet potato slices. Top with the remaining tempeh and Swiss chard, followed by the remaining sweet potato slices.

Combine milk, nutmeg, and black pepper. Pour over dish. Cover with foil and bake for 35 minutes. Remove foil, top with non-dairy mozzarella cheese and bake for an additional 15 minutes. Sprinkle with toasted flaxseed.

SWISS CHARD WITH GARLIC AND LEMON

serves: **4**

prep time: **10 minutes**

INGREDIENTS

2 pounds Swiss chard, chopped (stems and center ribs removed)

⅛ cup water

3 cloves garlic, chopped

1 tablespoon lemon juice

¼ teaspoon ground pepper

DIRECTIONS

In a large pan, sauté Swiss chard in water over medium heat until slightly wilted, about 1 minute, adding more water as necessary to prevent scorching. Stir in garlic. Cover and cook until tender, about 3 minutes, stirring occasionally. Uncover and cook another 1-2 minutes until liquid evaporates. Stir in lemon juice and pepper.

THAI VEGETABLE CURRY

serves: **6**

prep time: **40 minutes**

INGREDIENTS

4 cloves garlic, finely chopped

2 tablespoons finely chopped fresh ginger

2 tablespoons chopped fresh mint

2 tablespoons chopped fresh basil

2 tablespoons chopped fresh cilantro

2 cups carrot juice

1 red bell pepper, seeded and thinly sliced

1 large eggplant, peeled, if desired, and cut into 1-inch cubes

2 cups green beans, cut into 2-inch pieces

3 cups sliced shiitake mushrooms

1 (8-ounce) can bamboo shoots, drained

2 tablespoons Dr. Fuhrman's VegiZest or other no-salt seasoning

½ teaspoon curry powder

2 cups watercress leaves, divided

3 tablespoons unsalted natural chunky peanut butter

1-½ pounds firm tofu*, cut into ¼-inch slices

½ cup coconut water

½ cup chopped raw cashews

mint, basil or cilantro leaves, for garnish (optional)

DIRECTIONS

Place the garlic, ginger, mint, basil, cilantro, carrot juice, bell pepper, eggplant, green beans, mushrooms, bamboo shoots, VegiZest, curry powder, and 1 cup of the watercress in a wok or large skillet. Bring to a boil, cover, and simmer, stirring occasionally, until all the vegetables are tender. Mix in the peanut butter. Add the tofu, bring to a simmer, and toss until hot. Add the coconut water and heat through. Top with the remaining 1 cup watercress and the cashews. Garnish with mint, basil or cilantro leaves, if desired.

* One pound cooked chicken may be substituted for tofu.

Note: This can be served over brown rice, wild rice, or quinoa.

TOFU WITH
PUMPKIN SEED COATING

serves: **5**

prep time: **30 minutes**

INGREDIENTS

1 pound tofu, extra firm, sliced into 5 cutlets

-MARINADE-

3 tablespoons tahini

3 tablespoons balsamic vinegar

½ teaspoon lime juice, freshly squeezed

½ teaspoon garlic

pinch cayenne pepper

-CRUST-

1 cup pumpkin seeds, toasted*

2 tablespoons corn meal

1 teaspoon minced cilantro

½ teaspoon chili powder

¼ teaspoon cumin

¼ teaspoon crushed red pepper flakes

DIRECTIONS

Preheat oven to 350°F.

Place marinade ingredients in a 9"x13" casserole dish, whisk well, add tofu cutlets and allow to marinate for 15 minutes. Flip tofu and let sit for another 15 minutes. Place tofu and marinade in oven and bake for 10 minutes.

While tofu is baking, place pumpkin seeds in a food processor and pulse until crumbly (coarse texture). Remove seeds from food processor and combine with remaining crust ingredients.

Remove tofu from oven, cover liberally with crust mixture, return to oven and bake for an additional 10 minutes.

* *Toast pumpkin seeds in a large heavy skillet over medium high heat, stirring frequently, until seeds are puffed and beginning to brown, 2-4 minutes. Transfer to a large plate and cool.*

VEGETABLE BEAN BURRITO

serves: **6**

prep time: **20 minutes**

INGREDIENTS

1 head broccoli florets, chopped

½ head cauliflower florets, chopped

2 carrots, chopped

2 medium red bell peppers, seeded and chopped

1 medium zucchini, chopped

1 medium onion, chopped

4 cloves garlic, chopped

1½ tablespoons Dr. Fuhrman's VegiZest or other no-salt seasoning

1 teaspoon dried basil

1 teaspoon dried oregano

1 teaspoon dried parsley

1 cup raw cashews

½ cup unsweetened soy, hemp, or almond milk

1½ cups cooked pinto beans, or 1 (15-ounce) can, no-salt-added or low-sodium, drained and rinsed

6 whole wheat tortillas or large romaine lettuce leaves

no-salt-added or low-sodium salsa

DIRECTIONS

Place 2 tablespoons water, the broccoli, cauliflower, carrots, bell peppers, zucchini, onion, garlic, VegiZest, basil, oregano, and parsley in a large covered pot. Sauté for 15 minutes or until tender, adding more water if needed. In the meantime, place cashews and milk in a food processor or high-powered blender and blend until smooth. Add the cashew mixture and beans to the vegetables and mix thoroughly.

Spread the mixture on the tortillas and roll up to form burritos. Serve with salsa.

VEGETABLE GARBANZO WRAPS

serves: **4**

prep time: **20 minutes**

INGREDIENTS

1 large tomato, chopped

1 avocado, chopped

1 cucumber, chopped

4 leaves romaine lettuce, shredded

1½ cups garbanzo beans (chickpeas), mashed, or 1 (15-ounce) can, no-salt-added or low-sodium, drained and mashed

2 tablespoons fruit-flavored vinegar

4 whole grain tortillas

½ tablespoon raw sesame tahini

DIRECTIONS

Toss vegetables with garbanzo beans and vinegar. Warm a whole grain tortilla, spread a thin coating of tahini on it, and roll with the vegetable/bean mixture.

VEGETABLE SHEPHERD'S PIE

serves: **6**

prep time: **35 minutes**

INGREDIENTS

4 large sweet potatoes

1 cup fresh or frozen chopped broccoli

1 cup fresh or frozen sliced cauliflower

1 medium chopped leek

1 red bell pepper, cut into 1-inch squares

1 teaspoon Herbes de Provence (dried French herbs)

4 tablespoons Dr. Fuhrman's VegiZest or other no-salt vegetable soup base

2 cups water

2 cups fresh chopped spinach or 1 cup frozen, thawed and drained

½ cup carrot juice

4 teaspoons cornstarch

1 cup firm tofu, water squeezed out and crumbled

1 cup hazelnuts, Brazil nuts, or raw almonds, chopped medium fine (optional)

2 tablespoons chopped fresh parsley, for garnish

DIRECTIONS

Preheat oven to 375°F.

Bake sweet potatoes until soft, about 45 minutes. When potatoes are tender, remove to a bowl and mash. Set aside.

Place broccoli, cauliflower, leeks, bell peppers, Herbes de Provence, and Dr. Fuhrman's VegiZest in a large sauté pan along with 2 cups of water. Simmer until almost tender, about 10 minutes. (If using frozen broccoli and cauliflower, reduce water to 1-½ cups.) Add fresh or thawed, drained frozen spinach and toss.

Drain and remove vegetables, reserving vegetable liquid in pot. Whisk cornstarch into carrot juice and whisk into boiling vegetable liquid until it thickens. Add vegetables and crumbled tofu to sauce and toss to combine.

Divide mixture into two 8-inch pie pans. Top each with ¼ cup nuts. Spread sweet potatoes over the top and sprinkle with remaining nuts.

Bake at 375°F for 20-30 minutes until hot and nuts are light brown. If desired, sprinkle with parsley.

This dish may be prepared ahead and frozen, unbaked. Cover tightly with aluminum foil before freezing. Do not defrost, but bake an additional 10-15 minutes.

NON-VEGAN DISHES

GARDEN EGGS
AND TOFU WITH SALSA

serves: **3**

prep time: **25 minutes**

INGREDIENTS

½ medium onion, diced

1 medium zucchini, grated

1 carrot, grated

2 cups chopped Swiss chard or organic spinach

½ medium tomato, diced

2 cloves garlic, pressed

2 teaspoons Herbes de Provence (dried French herbs)

1 cup firm tofu

⅛ teaspoon curry powder, or more, to taste

4 eggs, beaten

¼ cup prepared salsa, low-sodium

1 ounce non-dairy mozzarella cheese, shredded

6 sprouted grain tortillas (optional)

DIRECTIONS

In a large sauté pan, heat ⅛ cup water and water sauté the onion, zucchini, carrot, and Swiss chard for about 2 minutes. Add the tomato, garlic, and herbs. Cook, stirring for about 2 minutes, until the vegetables begin to soften.

Squeeze water out of tofu and crumble.

Scatter the tofu over the vegetables and sprinkle with curry powder. Mix with vegetables and cook over high heat until water is cooked away.

Reduce heat to low and stir in the eggs, mixing well so the vegetables and tofu bind with the eggs. Continue stirring, until the eggs are cooked.

Top with salsa and grated non-dairy cheese.

May be served on sprouted grain tortillas.

MEDITERRANEAN FISH STEW

serves: **4**

prep time: **45 minutes**

INGREDIENTS

2 red bell peppers, sliced

2 medium onions, sliced

1 medium eggplant,
cut into 1-inch pieces

2 medium zucchini,
cut into 1-inch pieces

1 cup sliced mushrooms

6 medium tomatoes,
chopped

2 cloves garlic, finely
chopped

1 teaspoon Herbes de
Provence

¼ teaspoon black pepper

1 pound firm fish fillets,
cut into 1-inch pieces (such
as halibut, bass, salmon)

2 tablespoons fresh
chopped parsley

1 tablespoon fresh
lemon juice

DIRECTIONS

Heat ⅛ cup water in a large pan. Add the bell peppers and onions and cook for 3 minutes, add the eggplant, zucchini and mushrooms and continue cooking for another 6-8 minutes or until tender, adding more water if necessary to keep from sticking. Add the tomatoes, garlic, Herbes de Provence and black pepper and simmer on low heat for 4 minutes.

Add the fish to the stew and mix in gently. Cover and simmer on low heat for 8-10 minutes, stirring occasionally. Before serving, stir in parsley and lemon juice.

ORANGE KALE-CHOY CHICKEN

serves: **4**

prep time: **30 minutes**

INGREDIENTS

2-3 bunches kale, chopped (stems and center ribs removed)

10 ounces skinless, boneless chicken breasts, thinly sliced

2 cups fresh carrot juice

1 tablespoon Dr. Fuhrman's VegiZest

3 bunches baby bok choy, finely sliced

1 onion, finely sliced

4 cloves garlic, minced or pressed

1 teaspoon grated lemon zest

1 tablespoon fresh ginger root

pinch cayenne

1½ tablespoons arrowroot or cornstarch

½ cup orange juice

DIRECTIONS

Steam kale for 15 minutes and set aside. Spray nonstick pan lightly with olive oil and heat pan. Add small pieces of thin sliced chicken to hot pan and cook about 3 minutes per side until just cooked through. Remove to a plate and set aside. Add carrot juice, VegiZest, bok choy, onions, garlic, lemon zest, ginger, and cayenne to the pan, and simmer on high heat for 5 minutes to reduce to a lumpy sauce.

Mix arrowroot with orange juice and add to simmering sauce. Continue cooking until sauce thickens, about 2 more minutes. Add chicken to sauce and simmer for 3 more minutes. Serve chicken mixture spread atop a large bed of steamed kale.

ORIENTAL CHICKEN AND BROCCOLI

serves: **5**

prep time: **45 minutes**

INGREDIENTS

6 ounces skinless, boneless chicken breast

2 pounds fresh broccoli, stems and florets

1 cup water chestnuts, drained

1 cup baby corn, drained

1 cup sliced mushrooms

1 tablespoon sesame oil

1 egg white

1 tablespoon date sugar

1 tablespoon cornstarch

3 tablespoons chunky pineapple with juice

1 teaspoon Bragg Liquid Aminos

DIRECTIONS

Place chicken in small steamer and steam for 25 minutes, then dice into small chunks. Peel broccoli stems and cut florets and stems into pieces. Steam broccoli in a big pot for 15 minutes. Add the water chestnuts, baby corn, and mushrooms and steam for 5 minutes more.

Whip the sesame oil with the egg white. Fold in the date sugar, cornstarch, pineapple with juice, and Liquid Aminos. Mix and simmer on low heat for 3 minutes. Add chicken and egg white mixture to vegetables and toss.

THIS RECIPE GIVES 10 OUNCES OF VEGETABLES PER PERSON WITH ONLY 1½ OUNCES OF CHICKEN AS A FLAVORING. IT IS ALSO GOOD WITHOUT THE CHICKEN

SALMON AND VEGETABLES IN A PACKET

serves: **4**

prep time: **30 minutes**

INGREDIENTS

4 (4-ounce) salmon*
fillets or steaks

freshly ground pepper

1 teaspoon freshly
grated ginger root

juice of 1 lemon

2 ripe tomatoes, chopped

1 medium zucchini,
chopped

2 cups sliced mushrooms

1 medium red onion,
thinly sliced

1 clove garlic, minced
or pressed

4 cups coarsely chopped
mustard greens or Swiss
chard

4 sheets aluminum foil,
12"x24"

small amount of olive oil
or olive oil cooking spray

DIRECTIONS

Preheat the oven to 450°F.

Place the salmon fillets in a glass baking dish and add pepper, grated ginger, and lemon juice. In a large bowl, mix tomatoes, zucchini, mushrooms, red onion, and garlic. Fold each square of foil over to make a square of double thickness. Brush the center portion of each square with a small amount of olive oil. On each square, place 1 cup chopped mustard greens, one salmon fillet, and one quarter of the tomato/vegetable mixture. Fold the foil into airtight packets. Bake for 20 minutes.

Carefully avoiding the steam that will be released, open each packet and check that the fish is cooked. To serve, open the foil and transfer contents to a plate or bowl.

Any fish fillet may be used with this recipe.

SCRAMBLED VEGGIES AND EGGS

serves: **2**

prep time: **15 minutes**

INGREDIENTS

2 eggs

2 tablespoons unsweetened soy, hemp, or almond milk

½ red bell pepper, diced

2 onions, chopped

½ cup diced fresh tomatoes

½ cup diced fresh mushrooms

1 tablespoon Dr. Fuhrman's VegiZest or other no-salt seasoning

1 teaspoon Spike no-salt seasoning or other no-salt seasoning

4 ounces organic spinach, coarsely chopped, or baby spinach

DIRECTIONS

Beat eggs with soy milk. Water sauté the peppers, onions, tomatoes, mushrooms, VegiZest, and Spike in ⅛ cup water until vegetables are tender, adding water if necessary. Add spinach to wilt. Cook most water out of vegetables, add eggs, and stir until cooked through.

TURKEY SPINACH BURGERS

serves: **8**

prep time: **15 minutes**

INGREDIENTS

1 pound ground
turkey breast

10 ounces frozen,
chopped spinach,
defrosted and drained

¼ cup dried bread crumbs

1 cup cooked oatmeal

1 cup chopped onion

2 tablespoons chopped
fresh parsley

1½ tablespoons vegan
Worcestershire sauce
(found in health food
stores)

1 teaspoon hot sauce

DIRECTIONS

Combine all ingredients in a large bowl. Mix
well. Divide mixture into 8 or 16 portions and
form into patties. Coat grill rack or broiler pan
with cooking spray. Grill or broil until browned
on both sides, about 7 minutes per side.

TURKEY VEGETABLE MEATLOAF

serves: **8**

prep time: **20 minutes**

INGREDIENTS

20 ounces ground turkey

2 cups soft-cooked dark wild rice (black or mahogany)

10 ounces frozen organic chopped spinach, thawed and drained

1 large carrot, grated

1 medium green bell pepper, chopped

2 medium onion, chopped

2 eggs

1 cup diced white mushrooms

2 large cloves garlic, minced

6 tablespoons ketchup, low-sodium

2 tablespoons vegan Worcestershire sauce (found in health food stores)

1 tablespoon chopped fresh basil

1 teaspoon Dijon mustard

1 teaspoon Italian herb seasoning

½ teaspoon marjoram

¼ teaspoon black pepper

1½ cups diced tomatoes, or 1 (15-ounce) can, no-salt-added or low-sodium, drained

1 tablespoon ketchup, low-sodium

DIRECTIONS

Preheat oven to 350°F. Mix ground turkey and cooked rice together. Add remaining ingredients except for half of the tomatoes and ketchup. Mix well to combine. Shape into loaf and place in a large loaf pan, or spread in a tube pan. Top with remaining tomatoes mixed with 1 tablespoon of ketchup.

Bake for 1 hour and 15 minutes until meat is cooked through.

DESSERTS

APPLE SURPRISE

serves: **6**

prep time: **12 minutes**

INGREDIENTS

1 cup raisins

¼ cup water

8 apples, peeled, cored, and diced

½ cup chopped walnuts

4 tablespoons ground flaxseed

1 tablespoon cinnamon

DIRECTIONS

Place raisins in bottom of pot and cover with ¼ cup water. Place diced apples on top. Cover and steam over very low heat for 5 minutes. Transfer apples and raisins to a bowl, add the remaining ingredients, and mix well.

BANANA FIG "ICE CREAM"

serves: **4**

prep time: **6 minutes**

INGREDIENTS

5 dried figs, stems removed

4 ripe bananas, frozen*

¼ cup unsweetened soy, hemp, or almond milk

2 teaspoons Dr. Fuhrman's Black Fig Vinegar

DIRECTIONS

Blend all ingredients in a high-powered blender until creamy.

* Freeze peeled ripe bananas in plastic bag for at least 24 hours in advance.

BANANA NUT COOKIES

INGREDIENTS

¼ cup dates, pitted

¼ cup soy, hemp, or almond milk

1 cup walnuts

1 cup pecans

1 cup unsweetened shredded coconut

4 bananas

2 teaspoons cinnamon

DIRECTIONS

Cover dates with soy milk and soak overnight. Place the nuts and coconut in a food processor with the metal S blade and grind to a coarse meal. Add the bananas, dates with soy milk, and cinnamon. Mix to form the dough. Take the thick mixture out of the food processor and drop by spoonfuls onto a nonstick cookie sheet. Bake in the oven at 250°F for 30 minutes.

BLUEBERRY BANANA COBBLER

serves: **2**

prep time: **10 minutes**

INGREDIENTS

1 banana

1 cup frozen blueberries

¼ cup old-fashioned rolled oats

1 tablespoon currants

⅛ teaspoon vanilla

2 tablespoons chopped raw almonds

2 tablespoons unsweetened coconut

¼ teaspoon cinnamon

DIRECTIONS

Combine banana, berries, oats, currents, and vanilla in a microwave-safe dish. Microwave for 2 minutes. Top with almonds, coconut, and cinnamon. Microwave for 1 minute. Serve warm.

BLUEVADO PIE

serves: **8**
prep time: **20 minutes**

INGREDIENTS

-CRUST-

10 date/coconut rolls
(remove almonds)

1½ cups Familia
(Swiss baby muesli, no
added sugar)

-FILLING-

10 ounces frozen
blueberries

10 pitted dates, chopped

4-5 bananas

1 Haas avocado

1 tablespoon
unsweetened shredded
coconut

DIRECTIONS

-CRUST-
In a bowl, thoroughly blend the date/coconut
rolls and muesli. Transfer mixture to pie plate,
pressing down to make pie crust.

-FILLING-
In a high-powered blender, blend all filling
ingredients, except for coconut, until smooth. Pour
into the pie crust. Sprinkle with coconut.

Cover and freeze for at least 3 hours before
serving.

CHOCOLATE CHERRY "ICE CREAM"

serves: **2**

prep time: **5 minutes**

INGREDIENTS

½ cup vanilla soy, hemp, or almond milk

1 tablespoon natural cocoa powder

4 dates, pitted

1½ cups frozen dark sweet pitted cherries

DIRECTIONS

Blend all ingredients together in a high-powered blender or food processor until smooth and creamy. If using a regular blender, only put in about half the cherries at first. Blend until smooth. Add the remaining cherries a few at a time until the entire mixture is smooth.

Frozen berries may be used instead of cherries.

CHOCOLATE DIP

serves: **8**

prep time: **15 minutes**

INGREDIENTS

1½ cups whole
raw almonds

¾ cup vanilla soy,
hemp, or almond milk

2 cups organic
baby spinach

2 cups frozen
strawberries or
blueberries

⅔ cup dates, pitted

3 tablespoons
Dr. Fuhrman's Cocoa
Powder or other natural
cocoa powder

1 teaspoon vanilla extract

1 raw beet,
lightly steamed

DIRECTIONS

Blend nuts and soy milk until smooth. Add remaining ingredients and blend again. May be eaten as a pudding or used as a dip for fresh fruit and vegetables.

FROZEN BANANA FLUFF

serves: **2**
prep time: **5 minutes**

INGREDIENTS

¼ cup vanilla soy, hemp,
or almond milk

2 ripe bananas, frozen*

dash vanilla extract

2 tablespoons
ground flaxseed

DIRECTIONS

Place the soy milk in the food processor with the
S blade in place. Turn the machine on and drop
in small slices of the frozen bananas, one by
one. Add vanilla and combine until smooth and
creamy. Sprinkle ground flaxseeds on top.

* *Freeze peeled ripe bananas in a plastic bag
   at least 24 hours in advance.*

HEALTHY CHOCOLATE CAKE

serves: **12**

prep time: **40 minutes**

INGREDIENTS

-CAKE-

1⅔ cups whole wheat pastry flour

1 teaspoon baking powder

3 teaspoons baking soda

3½ cups pitted dates, divided

1 cup pineapple chunks in own juice, drained

1 banana

1 cup unsweetened applesauce

1 cup shredded beets

¾ cup shredded carrots

½ cup shredded zucchini

3 tablespoons Dr. Fuhrman's Cocoa Powder or other natural cocoa powder

½ cup currants

1 cup chopped walnuts

1½ cups water

2 teaspoons vanilla extract

-ICING-

1 cup raw macadamia nuts or raw cashews, unsalted

1 cup vanilla soy milk

⅔ cup pitted dates

⅓ cup Brazil nuts or hazelnuts

2 tablespoons Dr. Fuhrman's Cocoa Powder or other natural cocoa powder

1 teaspoon vanilla extract

DIRECTIONS

-CAKE-

Preheat oven to 350°F. Mix flour, baking powder, and baking soda in a small bowl. Set aside. In blender or food processor, purée 3 cups of dates with the pineapple, banana, and applesauce. Slice remaining ½ cup dates into ½-inch pieces. In large bowl, mix sliced dates, beets, carrots, zucchini, cocoa powder, currants, walnuts, water, vanilla, and flour mixture. Add the blended mixture and mix well. Spread in a 9½"x13½" nonstick baking pan. Bake for 1 hour or until a toothpick inserted into the center comes out clean.

-ICING-

Using a high-powered blender*, combine all icing ingredients until smooth and creamy. Place a dollop over warm cake and serve. If desired, you can spread it on cooled cake, too.

* A food processor may be used to combine icing ingredients, but the icing will not be as smooth.

MACADAMIA CREAM

serves: **8**
prep time: **5 minutes**

INGREDIENTS

1⅓ cups macadamia nuts

1 cup soy, hemp,
or almond milk

⅔ cup dates, pitted

DIRECTIONS

Blend nuts, soy milk, and dates together in a
high-powered blender. Serve over strawberries,
other berries, or fruit. It also can be used as a
topping on fruit sorbet or fruit compote, or as an
icing on a vegetable or fruit pie or cake.

FOR A DIFFERENT
FLAVOR, SUBSTITUTE
DRIED MANGOS
(UNSULFURED,
UNSUGARED) FOR HALF
THE DATES. SOAK THE
DRIED MANGOS IN THE
MILK OVERNIGHT

MIXED BERRY FREEZE

serves: **2**
prep time: **10 minutes**

INGREDIENTS

¼ cup soy, hemp,
or almond milk

½ ripe banana, frozen*

1 10-ounce package
of frozen mixed berries

2 tablespoons
ground flaxseed

DIRECTIONS

Place the soy milk in a food processor with the S blade in place. Turn the machine on and drop in small slices of frozen banana, one by one. Add the berries and continue to mix. Place in serving bowls and top with flaxseed.

* Freeze peeled ripe bananas in plastic bags at least 24 hours in advance. The same recipe also can be made with other frozen fruit.

PEACH SORBET

serves: **4**

prep time: **5 minutes**

INGREDIENTS

1 pound frozen peaches

¼ cup soy, hemp,
or almond milk

4 dates, pitted

DIRECTIONS

Blend ingredients in food processor or high-powered blender until smooth and creamy.

RED VELVET SORBET

serves: **4**

prep time: **10 minutes**

INGREDIENTS

4 large ripe bananas, frozen

10 ounces frozen raspberries

2 tablespoons Dr. Fuhrman's Cocoa Powder or other natural cocoa powder

4-5 dates, pitted, chopped

DIRECTIONS

Blend all ingredients in a high-powered blender until creamy. Refreeze briefly for 3-5 minutes.

STRAWBERRY PINEAPPLE SORBET

serves: **2**

prep time: **5 minutes**

INGREDIENTS

4 slices dried pineapple, unsweetened and unsulfured

½ cup orange juice

1 10-ounce bag frozen strawberries

1 cup fresh organic strawberries, sliced

DIRECTIONS

Soak dried pineapple in orange juice overnight or for a few hours. Blend all ingredients except fresh strawberries in a high-powered blender.

Pour into sorbet glasses, and top with sliced fresh strawberries.

SUMMER FRUIT PIE

serves: **8**

prep time: **30 minutes**

INGREDIENTS

-PIE SHELL-

1 cup almonds

1 cup dates, pitted (medjool preferred)

-PIE FILLING-

3 bananas, sliced

1 teaspoon lemon juice

2 kiwis, sliced

1 quart organic strawberries

1 pint blueberries

½ cup vanilla soy, hemp, or almond milk

½ bag frozen strawberries or 1 pint fresh organic strawberries

2 dates

DIRECTIONS

Make pie shell by placing almonds in a food processor and processing until very fine. Add dates and process until chopped and mixed well. Press mixture in a pie plate to form shell.

To make the filling, spread bananas on the crust, pressing down slightly. Sprinkle lemon juice over the bananas. Place kiwis, strawberries, and blueberries over the bananas. Place the soy milk, frozen strawberries, and dates in a blender and blend until smooth. Pour blended mixture over the fruit. Decorate with fruit as desired. Cover and freeze for at least 2 hours before serving.

WILD APPLE CRUNCH

INGREDIENTS

6 apples, peeled
and sliced

¾ cup chopped walnuts

8 dates, chopped

1 cup currants or raisins

¾ cup water

½ teaspoon cinnamon

¼ teaspoon nutmeg

juice of 1 orange

DIRECTIONS

Preheat oven to 375°F.

Combine all ingredients except the orange juice.
Place in a baking pan and drizzle the orange
juice on top. Cover and bake at 375°F for
about 1 hour until all ingredients are soft, stirring
occasionally.

YOU ALSO CAN
SIMMER THIS IN A
COVERED POT FOR 30
MINUTES ON TOP OF
THE STOVE, STIRRING
OCCASIONALLY

YUMMY BANANA OAT BARS

serves: **8**

prep time: **10 minutes**

INGREDIENTS

2 cups quick-cooking rolled oats (not instant)

½ cup shredded coconut

½ cup raisins or chopped dates

¼ cup chopped walnuts

2 large ripe bananas, mashed

¼ cup puréed apple

DIRECTIONS

Preheat oven to 350°F.

Mix all the ingredients in a large bowl until well combined. Press into a 9"x9" baking pan and bake for 30 minutes. Cool on a wire rack. When cool, cut into squares or bars.

Now that you have learned how to make all of the delicious recipes in this book, I hope that you will experiment and make variations and new recipes all on your own. The high-nutrient and other dietary guidelines in this book will help you chart a path toward superior nutrition and superior health. (The companion book, *3 Steps to Incredible Health, Volume 1*, has even more detailed information.)

You deserve a lot of credit for making the effort necessary to step out of the crowd and make a strong commitment to yourself. Each of us has within us a strong inner voice that urges us to survive and to thrive. But most people do not know the best way to respond. You have answered the call, and you know how to respond. Your response will pay big dividends in improved health and enhanced longevity.

Living as we do, surrounded by people who are looking for instant pleasure and effortless solutions to problems, the steady step-by-step diet and health transformation you are undertaking sometimes may seem like an insurmountable task. But as you progress, you will reach the point where renewed joy, vibrancy, and enthusiasm will be your loyal companions. Keep practicing your newly acquired knowledge, and soon it will become your new way of eating and living. If you have been following the menu plans, you are probably feeling a lot better already. Use that as motivation to strive to feel even better.

Don't underestimate your body's powerful capacity for self-healing. When superior nutrition becomes your normal way of eating, you give yourself the opportunity to restore more youthful health and recover from chronic illnesses that many doctors think are "incurable."

Remember, as tremendous as it is, your new knowledge about health is only a first step. You must put this new knowledge into practice and repeat your new beneficial behaviors until they become a part of you. You and I know that it is not easy to develop new habits, and there is no shortcut to developing new skills and expertise. However, if you truly desire to create the "new you," persevere despite any obstacles or temporary setbacks. You don't need to be perfect; you just need to keep on trying. Step-by-step, moment-by-moment, day-by-day, you truly can make your life better and better.

Wishing you much happiness and a long, healthy, and pleasurable life—*it can be yours!*

FOR MORE INFORMATION, VISIT:

www.DrFuhrman.com

Dr. Fuhrman's official website for information,
recipes, supportive services, and products.

Or call:

(800) 474-WELL (9355)

NOTES

NOTES